Menopause & Emotions

Making sense of your feelings
when your feelings make no sense.

Lafern Page
BEd., M.A.

PRIMAVERA PRESS

Published by Primavera Press,
P.O. Box 74672,
2803 West 4th Avenue,
Vancouver, B.C., Canada, V6K 4P4

Cover design by Harry Bardal
Typesetting by CompuType
Printed and bound in Canada by Best Gagne Book Manufacturers Inc.

Canadian Cataloguing in Publication Data

Page, Lafern, 1941-

Menopause and emotions

Includes bibliographical references and index.

ISBN 0-9697874-0-5
1. Menopause—Psychological aspects. 2. Menopause —Social aspects.
I. Title.
RG186.P33 1994   618.1'75   C94-910073-0

This book is dedicated to

my mother,

to women who have had to make hard choices

in their lives, and to their

daughters and sons, with love.

TABLE OF CONTENTS

Acknowledgements

This book was made possible by the many women who shared with me their stories and experiences. In particular, I wish to acknowledge The First Group. The memory of their voices, along with their courage and commitment to exploring the depths of their experiences has stayed with me throughout the writing of this book.

I have attempted to build on research which explores the felt experiences of women. In doing so, I am grateful to the following authors/researchers who are among the many who have informed this work: Diane Barthel; Mary Field Belenky, Blythe McVicker Clinchy, Nancy Rule Goldberger and Jill Mattuck Tarule; Susan Brownmiller; Janine O'Leary Cobb; Rita Freedman; Carol Gilligan; Emily Martin; Elissa Melamed; Adrienne Rich, Jean Baker Miller; Anne Wilson Schaef; Jane Ussher; and Paula Weideger.

Over the past three years, many good people have believed in both me and this book and, in doing so, have contributed in their various special ways to the writing of this book:

Joanne Broatch, for her enthusiasm, perceptive editing, and for joining me in turning writing/publishing into a playful experience;

My son, Buck, for always knowing his mom could do it;

Jack, for his humor and encouragement;

My sisters Jeannie and Teresa, and brother Ken for their love and support over the air waves;

My "cabin" friends, Rose Desrochers and Catherine Witsel, for the laughter we shared in some of the darker moments; Rose for her wisdom and clarity which helped me bring many thoughts to fruition; Linda Davidson for the warmth of her support;

The writers in my life who introduced me to the world of writing: my aunt Adelaide Schartner, Robbie and Carolyn Wolfe, Sheila Jacobs and Kathy Tees, for their understanding of the process and consistent encouragement. Sheila joined with me in a valuable process of mutual writing support;

Judith Daniluk and Sandra Butler, for first encouraging me to research and write about menopause;

In addition to those named above, I wish thank the following who also, at various times over the past three years, have given me valued feedback on the manuscript: Wendy Barrett, Kathy Brunton, Jean Burgess, Trish Crawford, Linda Davidson, Fran Diamond, Carol Herbert, Joan Jones, Joane Humphrey, Jean McKerracher, Susanne Montemuro, Christine O'Rourke, Ingrid Pacey, Jerilynn Prior, Adrianne Ross and Diane Waterman. My apologies to anyone I have forgotten.

Finally, thank you to those who helped with 11th hour proofreading.

An Invitation

Women's experiences of menopause—like their experiences of menstruation—vary widely. This book is not an attempt to translate your experience. That is for you to do, as we are each our own best expert in our bodies/our selves. Nor is this book about generalizing all women's experiences. Rather, the intent is to share some perspectives toward understanding this "change of life" on a deeper level.

The last combined physical-emotional-psychological-social process we all shared was beginning menstruation. Not all women experience what can follow: sex, pregnancy, marriage, childbirth or motherhood. Yet all of us stop menstruating, the average process being a slowing down over a period of four to seven years. Menopause is the only unique-to-women experience besides menstruation that we all share. Menstruation comes at a time when we are very young and usually ill-equipped to understand its role and significance in our lives. This is not the case with menopause. The experience of menopause usually comes later in life and presents a unique opportunity to better understand ourselves as women, both individually and collectively. You are invited to join in this journey either on your own or in the company of other women.

PART 1

1
Beyond
Positive
Thinking

There are many sides to menopause: physical, emotional, social-cultural, and developmental. Although these sides interact with each other to influence how we go through menopause, only the physical has received serious attention in our mainstream society. As a result, other aspects of menopause have remained out of sight, leaving us without an understanding of how the *interaction* of all these aspects affect our physical and emotional experiences of menopause. This book is an attempt to begin to correct this imbalance.

Some say that menopause is out of the closet now. I disagree. I say, at most, one arm is out, waving for attention. So far, many of us feel more comfortable talking about physical symptoms than about the other ways in which menopause may be affecting us. And "health talk" remains the most socially-acceptable way of discussing menopause. This makes sense because physical symptoms are the only part of menopause which has received attention by society at large.

Important factors affecting our menopause which have been largely ignored are:

– What menopause means to us, as women;

- The ways in which cultural values and beliefs associated with menopause affect us physically and emotionally; and,
- The role menopause plays in our psychological, physical and spiritual development as women.

Along with our personal history and circumstances, the social-cultural and developmental sides of menopause determine what menopause means to us. These meanings, in turn, influence *how* we go through menopause—including what we call a problem and what we do about it. And our emotions reflect what an experience means to us. Many women's ordinary emotions are heightened or magnified during menopause, especially in the early years. These heightened emotions are often assumed to be caused by "raging hormones."

This not only suggests there is a problem with women's bodies, but it perpetuates the idea that we are ruled by changing hormones and are therefore unstable. Because, as a culture, we have not given attention to the other-than-physical sides of menopause, I believe we need to re-examine this assumption and to seriously consider the extent to which we may be having *natural* responses to *unhealthy* external circumstances. Then, we can begin to explore the ways in which changing hormones interact with cultural values and beliefs to determine our physical and emotional experiences of menopause.

Currently, certain attitudes exist about how women *should* go through menopause. In our majority culture this ideal is usually, the less we notice it, the better. The verbal and nonverbal messages we receive are to keep busy, get in shape, cultivate both a positive attitude and a sense of humor and don't, whatever we do, inflict our emotional state on others.

While the reasoning behind these ideas may be understandable, I believe there is a danger in ignoring some significant realities buried in what menopause *means* in our majority culture. Another popular message is that it is unhealthy to look at what we are leaving behind as we go into menopause: that by looking back we risk having a sad, regretful and miserable menopause.

For many of us, these "shoulds" can play a role in keeping us quiet about some of our deeper feelings. When we insist that menopause is or should be a positive experience we can unintentionally encourage women to keep silent if they are not feeling positive. Strong societal forces act on us as we go through menopause and age. When these forces remain unnamed they have the power to keep us silent. As a result, there is a very real possibility that the surveys and questionnaires used by researchers to learn about women's attitudes toward menopause will reflect *society's* ideals rather than a woman's reality.

Some of us, not surprisingly, may feel that it is better to keep silent about how we are feeling, emotionally, during menopause rather than risk adding ammunition to a sexist arsenal.[1] And some of us in the age of feminism may genuinely feel that we *should not* be influenced or affected by menopause, believing that to do so would be like denying sexual equality, or agreeing that "biology is destiny."

Many of us have struggled to be recognized for qualities and abilities in addition to those associated with our bodies. However, pressing for equality has lead some of us to discount the biological differences between sexes. In the process, we may have downplayed or ignored our physical experiences. However, we need a balance. All of us must feel completely free to emotionally experience our menopause. But we must not be accused of being unliberated, of being over-identified with our fertility, or of being at the mercy of our hormones.

Opening the door to the menopause closet so that we can see its depths might expose the often shadowy realm of cultural values and beliefs. Once we identify these cultural values and beliefs they will lose some of their power and influence. Then we can more clearly see the significant role this transition plays in our development as women.

2
Beginning the Journey

I f we ask a woman what menopause means to her, we'll probably hear something like: "Menopause means I don't have my periods—and I'm happy to be done with them!" Or: "Menopause means I can't have any more kids. And the thought of having a child at *my* age *does* not appeal to me!" So menopause shouldn't be a big deal. Right? Yet, many of us find that when we have the opportunity to safely explore our deeper feelings about menopause, a different picture emerges.

Asking a woman what her menopause means to her is like asking someone, "Who are you?" Few of us will have ready answers because the question requires deep exploration and the answers need time to develop. Questions about meanings can also be difficult for researchers. Traditional methods of research do not lend themselves to explorations what our experiences mean to us and how those meanings influence us physically and emotionally. Adding to the problem is that menopause has a long history of silence and stereotyping in our majority culture. This history continues to affect a great many of us despite recent flurries of publicity about menopause.

I first became interested in menopause when I went through my own. Later, in 1988, I decided to do my graduate studies research on what menopause meant to women. I came to the conclusion that one of the best ways to uncover these meanings was to have women share their experiences with each other. I arranged to meet with a group of women once a week for several months. This process was so powerful that in the years since, I have continued to work with groups—now numbering hundreds of women—who embarked on the same journey to explore their menopause in the company of other women. This book is a product of those experiences.

By exploring the meanings of our menopause in this way, we, as women, came to see our midlife/menopause more clearly. We came to see it as an *interaction* between our bodies and our emotions, between ourselves and our culture, and as part of our development as female persons. As a result, we invariably felt calmer, stronger and more in control of our lives.

Many of the women in these groups had completed menopause and were able to look back on it with some perspective. As a result of talking about their experiences, hearing those of others and discussing what they had in common, they concluded that menopause had played a far greater role in their lives than they had realized while they were *in* menopause.

We all found ourselves wondering how different our menopause might have been had we known more about the experiences of other women. We had a gut feeling that we should have had a foundation of accumulated knowledge from generations of women—much as we have about cooking, child-rearing or homemaking. Instead, each of us felt as though we had gone through this transition as the first and only ones to do so, re-inventing the wheel each time.

About Meanings

Yellow roses fill me with happy thoughts and bring a flush to my cheeks because they take me back to the bloom of first love. My friend, on the other hand, associates the same flowers with the death of her mother; they fill her with sadness and cause her stomach to contract.

There is no particular need for us individually or as a society to understand the meanings two women attach to yellow roses, or how these meanings affect them. But menopause is different. Here, for us to understand the meaning—with its power to influence our bodies, minds and emotions—is essential. Tens of thousands of women are in menopause or are approaching it. And many of us, in our majority culture at least, are trying to make informed decisions about whether or not to take extra hormones. We are faced with conflicting expert opinions on the potential benefits or dangers of hormone therapy. Such decisions cannot be truly informed until we take questions of meaning into account. How does menopause affect how we feel about ourselves *as women?* What value do we place on being in menopause? How do we see menopause influencing our lives now? In the future? What do we think it means to those closest to us? What options do we feel we have? What role does it play in our development as women? How does all this affect us physically?

These are questions and issues with powerful implications not only for our health and peace of mind, but for our health care systems and for how we view, discuss and treat ourselves and other women as we age. And unless we understand all sides of menopause, we run the risk of taking medication for symptoms which may have more to do with the stress of *social and cultural* factors than with biological menopause alone.

Making sense of our emotions during menopause means understanding what we bring to it in the way of personal history, as well as what it means in the society in which we live. Three things that contribute to reaching this understanding are covered in this book.

One is to learn from others who have already explored this territory. As each of us is unique, you may or may not feel what the women quoted in this book felt. As you read, you may find yourself thinking, "Yes, that's how I feel!" Or, "No, that's not me." In any case, as you accept what fits and reject what does not, you will have a framework within which you can reflect on your menopause.

A second is to understand what meaning you bring to menopause in the way of beliefs and values from our dominant North American culture. Although we have many subcultures here in North America, the majority culture influences all of us—and it most certainly plays a role in the menopause experiences of most Canadian and American women. How menopause is defined and described in our culture has enormous implications for the meanings we, as individuals, attach to it. These descriptions and definitions provide us with road maps for our menopause. Although many factors go into determining how we personally experience menopause, to some extent each of our experiences sits on this common foundation: what being in menopause and what life beyond menopause means in our majority culture.

Perhaps because of our pioneering history, those of us in the mainstream society tend to see ourselves as individualists largely unaffected by our culture. But the fact is, our culture shapes our views about such basic things as reality, time, life, death, men, women, our bodies and health—as well as how we view life's transitions. And these concepts are not viewed in the same way in all cultures. In addition, culture strongly influences our values: what we call good or bad, rational or irrational, beautiful or ugly.

A third aspect in understanding your menopause is to learn what you have brought to it from your personal history. The many ways to explore this are discussed in the last chapter of this book.

Women Together: A Powerful Mix

Moving through menopause has been traditionally an individual and a mostly-silent experience for many of us. Changing that experience requires breaking that silence. Understanding its meaning requires talking to other women.

Meeting with other women to explore menopause can have many advantages. A small, trusted group with a common focus, meeting over time, provides an ideal setting for exploring the heart of a matter—because it encourages us to provide much more than just a description of our experiences. A group can provide the space and the motivation for us to understand our individual experiences in relation to those of others.

Throughout history we have told others of the events in our lives—whether around a camp fire at night or over coffee in a restaurant. When we share our experiences and listen to those of others we learn more about ourselves and the world around us. Telling our stories provides us, the tellers, with another perspective on ourselves because we hear our own voices and feel, see and hear the responses of others. In this way we come to know what role and meaning our experiences have in our lives, and to make sense of them.

Another benefit to meeting in a group is that it can break the power of the negative stereotype of the menopausal woman. Wanting to avoid being thought of as this stereotype has meant that many of us quite naturally prefer to keep to ourselves how we are actually feeling. Being in a trusted group can help overcome these natural concerns. The most common response I've heard when women meet in these groups is, "I thought I was the only one who felt that way!"

Recent research has shown that many of the ways we, as women, view the world and draw conclusions about truth, knowledge and authority differ from those of men. In order to uncover what menopause means to us, we must explore our experiences in our own way and come to our own conclusions based on those experiences. As Jean Baker Miller notes in her book, *Toward A New Psychology of Women*, there are many things that we, as women, know but have not yet put into words. Therefore, it is important that we start from our own experience, particularly when our feelings are involved, and *especially when our feelings may not make sense to us at first*.

And, as Belenky, Clinchy, Goldberger and Tarule discuss in their book, *Women's Ways of Knowing*, it is through *talking, listening* and *discussing* that many of us come to value and strengthen our own thoughts and experiences. Membership in a group can help us to make sense of what may feel confusing or unacceptable. It can also help overcome the silence and isolation linked to the other-than-physical sides of menopause.

Menopause = Change

All change involves both losses and gains; there must be one before there can be the other. Therefore, menopause encompasses what we lose, or leave behind and what we will gain, or move toward. Because this book is based on women's actual experiences, it naturally includes both the "negative" as well as the "positive" sides of their menopause. As you read the chapters about what they were leaving behind, keep in mind that transitions—and menopause is a transition—can be made much easier when we have an understanding of just what we feel we are losing or leaving behind. Doing this can help us to see the gains more clearly, as well as increase the possibilities and potentials for the future.

Clarifications

I use the term, "menopause" in the way most of us use it: referring to the years during which we cease to menstruate (as opposed to the medical definition which refers to a point in time, one year after our last period). "Menopause" also refers to natural versus artificial menopause (menopause brought on by surgery, radiation or chemotherapy). I use the terms "estrogen therapy," and "combined hormone therapy" (estrogen and progestins) instead of "estrogen replacement therapy" and "hormone replacement therapy". As Janine O'Leary Cobb notes in her 1993 edition of her book, *Understanding Menopause,* "Estrogen administered to women who go through natural menopause at the expected age replaces nothing, since it is perfectly normal for estrogen to be reduced at this time of life."[2] The term "replacement" is part of the language of disease which surrounds menopause and implies that our hormonal state as menopausal women is abnormal and must be fixed. I do believe that hormone therapy is a valuable resource for many women having a difficult menopause. However, as I will discuss further in Chapters 18 and 19, I disagree with the *assumption* that *all* women having a natural menopause should take extra hormones.

My intention with this book is to explore the non-physical sides of menopause because they have been obscured by the prevailing focus on physical symptoms. These other sides of menopause have the potential to influence our physical and emotional experiences of menopause. However, by focusing on the emotional, developmental and social-cultural sides of menopause, I do not mean to suggest that our physical experiences are not important, or that they have less significance, or that they are *caused* by emotions or social factors. On the contrary, I have come to believe our physical changes and genetics *interact* with what menopause *means* to us. These meanings come from a mixture of our personal history, present circumstances and societal beliefs and values. And one way these meanings surface is in our emotions.

Menopause is only one of many issues in our lives, and naturally it will vary in degree of importance among us. A great many of us are struggling with such basics as keeping ourselves and our children alive and well. For many of us, our needs to understand and *cope* with our menopause may be over-shadowed by our needs for adequate housing, child care, health programs and employment, to say nothing of emotional and financial support. This does not mean, as I've often heard suggested, that those of us who have increased emotional needs or are otherwise troubled by menopause do so because we have too much time on our hands. Nor is having good health or an easy menopause a sign of moral superiority or virtue. To have these attitudes insults and demeans *all* women.

Off and on in the writing of this book, I found myself with a nagging doubt that often left me feeling insecure and unsure. I could hear a voice that said, "Here we go again: one more white, heterosexual, middle-class Anglo-Saxon woman talking about an experience shared by all women—and, in the process, appearing to presume to speak for all women." This is not my intent. Women of other cultures and subcultures can and will speak for themselves. My purpose here is to shed light on the less visible aspects of many women's experiences of menopause in the *predominantly white, heterosexual, middle class North American culture* (this culture is alternately referred to as the "majority," "dominant," or "mainstream" culture). While I suspect that this majority culture also, to varying degrees, affects the experiences of those who live in its shadow, this book does not purport to address their menopause.

Because of popular assumptions and attitudes about menopause, some of the women's words and the ideas discussed in this book may seem, at first, difficult to understand or relate to. Please remember these thoughts and reflections have come from a process. They are not what these women might have written on a questionnaire or answered to questions asked "out of the blue." The women quoted in this book explored their menopause over a period of weeks, often months, in a process of mutual search and discovery to come to the statements quoted here.

The Common Themes

You will hear many women's voices in the following pages. Their physical experiences of menopause ranged from unremarkable to difficult. The circumstances of their lives were also very different. Many lived with a partner; others lived alone. Most were heterosexual, but some were lesbian. A majority had children, and some had none. Their ages spanned a range of 18 years. Some had early menopause, others late; most were "on time." Most of the groups were a mixture of all types of experience and lifestyle. Despite these differences, their emotional and social experiences of menopause were remarkably similar, tending to vary more in degree than in kind. Over the years of each woman's menopause these themes were more noticeable at some times than at others.

These common themes became evident over a number of weeks as the women told their stories, and discussed and reflected in a supportive setting. (The phrase, "the women" is used throughout this book and refers to the majority of the women I have worked with over the years.) Throughout the duration of each group, the focus was on what the women were *actually feeling, or had felt*, rather than on what they thought they *should have* felt.

The analogy of peeling an onion is useful in describing when and how the common themes emerged as the women talked about their experience of menopause. Like an onion, the many layers of menopause are hard to separate; the outer protects the inner core; it takes time to peel them back; and the act of peeling can bring tears to your eyes.

The outer, most easily-identified layers were the

women's physical experiences of menopause. They felt most noticeable and important and so were most easily talked about. The next layers to appear were the many ways the women were affected by insufficient information and the negative stereotype of the menopausal woman. In a deeper layer, and more difficult to reach and talk about, were feelings related to womanhood, femininity and sexuality. The experiences of those who had finished menopause suggest that menopause has a powerful role in our evolving development over the lifespan—and these experiences suggest a potential for increased freedom, strength and creativity.

* * * * * * * * * *

There are several ways you can use this book. I recommend you begin by reading most or all of it on your own. You may prefer to do the exercises on your own. Or you may decide to follow the guidelines for meeting other women outlined in Appendix A. These guidelines are intended to promote the creation of a discussion group (as opposed to a therapy or problem solving group) and are designed to encourage equality, trust and safety for all the members.

Or you may wish to get together with a group of women to read and discuss the book together, chapter by chapter.

My invitation is to use this book in whatever way you like. My hope is that by doing so you will enjoy a wider and richer perspective on menopause.

It has been said that the function of emotions is to

dramatize our existence.[3]

How, then, shall we view the emotions of menopause?

3

When Women's Emotions Don't Seem To Make Sense, Why Do We Blame Their Hormones?

Not all women have heightened emotions during menopause. For those of us who do, are "raging hormones" responsible? We don't know the answer. The women I have worked with agree that it certainly *felt* as though their hormones were the cause of their emotions, because often how they were feeling didn't make sense to them. This is an understandable assumption because the way we talk and think about menopause has been so focused on the physical. Therefore, it is natural for us to look for physically-based answers. This is not to say that these answers are incorrect, but they may be incomplete.

When we recognize that menopause is far more than just a biological change, and that it comes with cultural values and beliefs, we then need to pay more attention to the ways in which emotions affect hormones. How do personal and cultural meanings associated with menopause—which show up in our emotions—affect our physical and emotional experiences of menopause?

The "raging hormones" question needs to be turned around so that we also ask: to what extent are heightened emotions a natural reaction to unhealthy cultural attitudes? To what extent do our emotions affect our hormones? Stressful emotions, for example, can bring on a hot flash or influence its severity. Do we assume too quickly that there is a problem with our *body*, which implies it needs treatment, instead of with mainstream attitudes and values about menopause? These questions make it imperative that we explore all sides of menopause—and at least entertain the idea that our emotions during menopause may be a natural reaction to personal/cultural circumstances, rather than a problem with our menopausal body. Regardless of what emerges from research into the purely physical side of menopause, what will remain is the need to understand what menopause means to us and how those meanings influence our menopause.

The emotions felt by the women in the groups I met with were not unusual or peculiar to menopause—they had experienced them throughout their lives at one time or another and for various reasons. The difference was that they felt them *more intensely* during menopause, and particularly during the first years. As with the other common themes, not all the women felt these emotions to the same degree. However, whether in large or small doses, their feelings were connected to their experience of menopause. Their emotions overlapped and cause, effect and inter-relationship were woven together.

I've often heard it said that some women *use* menopause as "an excuse to become inactive, go to fat, beg off sex, and sulk."[4] These women are then charged with contributing to the negative stereotype of the menopausal woman.

None of us want to be a party to giving menopause a bad name, so such comments can keep many of us quiet about some of our deepest feelings. I suggest that if some of us become "inactive, go to fat, beg off sex, and sulk," we do so for a good reason. And the sooner we look to the reason, the sooner we will break the taboos which still cling to menopause. Women who react to menopause are not sick or inferior, but are responding to the combined physical, emotional, social and cultural experience of menopause which is powerful, real and sometimes difficult.

An Introduction to the Women's Emotions

Here is an overview of some of the emotions the women talked about. The whys, the implications and the consequences of these emotions, and more, are detailed in the chapters that follow.

Feeling "needy"

Having needs is natural. The needs felt by the women I've worked with, like their emotions, were not unique to their menopause: they had experienced them off and on throughout much of their adult lives. Again, the difference was that they felt them more intensely during menopause. However, it was often difficult for them to name these needs. Even those who were past menopause had this difficulty.

Jean Baker Miller, in *Toward a New Psychology of Women,* notes that many of us have a hard time recognizing and clarifying our own needs, either to ourselves or to others. And if these needs are highly charged with emotion, they may be particularly difficult for us to figure out. Miller and other researchers have found that it is common for many of us, as females, to learn at a young age that we should devote ourselves to the care and empowerment of others. Anything else suggests selfishness. Many, if not most, of us come to menopause with a lifetime of setting our own needs aside to look after those of others. As a result, we often have little idea what our own needs might be.

One need expressed by the women in the groups was for role models to help them through this phase of their lives. They wanted to hear, in detail, how other women negotiated this transition. I believe they were expressing a natural longing. Throughout our lives we need people who have gone before us to provide a sense of direction, to serve as guides, to lessen our fears of the unknown. In this way, we learn that someone whom we like and respect survived what we are going through, and that we too will survive.

Another related need the women expressed was for more information, particularly about the experiences of other women. Too often they didn't get what they needed from the people or places they turned to for help and their questions far outnumbered any answers they received. This was a source of considerable frustration and influenced *how* they experienced menopause.

"I needed to know that there were *all kinds* of ways women go through menopause. I *didn't* need the articles in magazines that said it was nothing, or that I should just exercise more, or to change to my attitude."

"When I was in menopause I needed what I've heard

in this group: other women's experiences. I didn't need any pat responses that say, if you're having this, take that."

"Why do I find myself in menopause knowing so little about it! Something's not right here."

"Menopause *never* entered my head at that stage of the game. Never. I knew precious little about menopause then. I never thought that any of what I was going through might be related to menopause. Now I know that's what was happening."

"If I'd known [about the range of possible] menopause experiences, I would have felt much better, or differently at least. I missed realizing that it's okay for your nerves to be bad, that many other women feel that way and that I wasn't crazy."

The following dialogue occurred between two women I'll call Ann and Sara:
"With kids in puberty we say, 'Oh, well, he's going through adolescence. Give him a bit of time, give him a bit of space.' But women in menopause don't have that. We're made to feel guilty about being in the menopause when our emotions erupt. . . . You should be given space during that time, and you're not. . . . The family needs to know that during that time, those days, that they lay off. Leave you be."
Ann: "That's right! That's the closest anybody has come to [expressing] how I feel. I need my family to back off during those times!"
Sara: "That's right. And you should have time out."
Ann: "Let me be! "
Sara: "Like, 'Look here, I may need five years, but

you guys back off because I'm, I'm out of order!' There's a great need for education about this. Sometimes we need that elbow room. And it's really important."
Ann: "I was very crowded for those years, and it pissed me off. So if people had backed off more—the way you find in a professional environment, more so than in your own home—I would have had a lot more peace of mind. But I had no idea at the time. I had no idea until Sara said it. That's all I needed. Just leave me be. Leave me be. That was one of my biggest needs."

Both Sara and Ann had had a difficult menopause. Interestingly, most of the women—regardless of their ease or difficulty with menopause—felt much like these two women, albeit with less intensity. As they pointed out, they may not have said it at the time, but they felt it. They identified with the confusion of feeling "needy" while, at the same time, wanting others to "back off." Again, they felt irrational because they were in the double bind of simultaneously wanting to be hugged and wanting to be left alone. As I will discuss later, this need for more "space" begins to make sense when we understand the role menopause plays in our development as women.

The changes the women were going through affected their relationships with others—particularly their partners:

"During menopause I was very aware of having a lot of needs. I hated feeling so darn needy, so I spent more time alone than I ever had before."

"I had lost patience with being pleasant or calm or quiet. So, the proximity of people to me far more often triggered my being upset than it did my wanting an interplay or exchange of some sort with them."

"Sometimes I just can't stand to be touched. Sometimes I need not to be touched. How do tell your partner that?"

"I felt that if I talked about how I was really feeling during menopause, I'd just bring everybody down. Mostly I kept how I felt to myself. Besides, I didn't think anyone else would understand when I hardly did myself."

Being in a strong, supportive relationship in which their partner clearly valued them beyond youth or sex was a positive factor for both the heterosexual and lesbian women I have worked with.

Feeling confused and vulnerable

"I felt so confused at certain times during the early years of my menopause. If someone had said to me, you know, you're crazy, I probably would have believed them! I just found myself being very emotional a lot of the time."

"When I started my menopause I found that a lot of what had been familiar to me disappeared. I had no cycle anymore, yet I was still menstruating....I could find no organization in it. I didn't know from one day to the next what I was going to feel like. I got terribly annoyed very quickly....I just kept saying to my partner, this person you're looking at now isn't me. What bothered me was that I never knew when

I was going to *emerge* from this. How long was I going to feel this way?"

"They were very confusing years for me. I didn't know what was going on for me, what was happening to me then. Looking back, [my menopause] showed up more as emotional, like mood swings and crying jags, instead of physical."

From a woman who was postmenopausal at 35: "My doctor said, 'I'm very sorry, but you have *completed* menopause.' I was devastated. I was absolutely *devastated* (crying). I was so confused. I felt very vulnerable. . .It was like everything was signed, sealed and delivered. And I didn't even know anything about it!"

"I was going through so much *emotional* distress during that time, that I might have been totally unaware of the changes my body was going through. I felt extremely vulnerable about what was happening to me and about who, or what, I was becoming."

Feeling confused was one of the central themes in the women's experiences: they felt uncertain about why they were more emotional, about what was happening to their bodies and about whether they should be *doing* anything about it. Was what they were feeling related to menopause or to something else? They didn't have the information they needed and they wanted to know about other women's experiences so they could have some idea about what to expect. They were doubly confused if menopause felt like a "big deal" to them because they had learned that, as modern women, it *should not* be important—or, if they felt it was, there was something wrong with them. Some of the lesbian women experienced an additional "should": this was the expectation that because they were lesbian they would not be troubled with the same issues as heterosexual women. And, in some cases this was true. However, when they were troubled by the same issues, this "should" made them vulnerable to both silence and shame—as "shoulds" do to all of us, regardless of sexual orientation.

When the women found their ordinary emotions magnified for reasons that were not clear, they felt confused and, therefore, vulnerable. What was once only irritation became anger, even rage. Complicating these experiences was a message many of us receive at an early age: that it is honorable or mature to control or shut down emotions, particularly the so-called negative emotions of anger and sadness.

The women found the conflicting expert opinions on hormone therapy especially frustrating. To take or not to take? What are the benefits and risks? There are no clear and agreed-upon answers to these questions. And it is natural for women to feel confused and angry by this situation—especially when 52% of the total world population will go through this transition. What would it *feel* like to us as women if there was as much known about menopause as there is about making war?

In particular, women who have an early menopause may go for years without knowing what is happening to them. One woman reported visiting several physicians to find out what was happening to her, asking, could it be menopause? She was consistently told that she was too young.

"It was [the difference between] night and day when I finally found out [what was happening]. It was easier to take then. I felt sorrow, and loss, and confusion, and I still felt *vulnerable* all the time. But when I *knew* something was happening with my hormones, I knew I wasn't crazy. It made a *huge* difference to me. . . . If I had known that you guys [the group members] were going through something even remotely similar, it would have made a big difference to me. . . .The stuff in the pamphlets in doctor's offices is mostly irrelevant. It assumes you're making your own self miserable. I needed recognition that I was grieving and confused and I needed to talk about what was happening. And a hug isn't enough—nice, but not enough. A pep talk about exercise or positive thinking, etc., is not what I needed. At worst it's condescending, at best it didn't address the real issues."

A void is created when information and understanding are missing. And that void is vulnerable to being flooded with misinformation, "myths," and stereotypes. Naturally such a situation can lead to confusion, fear and anger. When we don't have adequate knowledge about what is happening to us, we can become frightened, feel isolated from others and begin to question our own perceptions and inner wisdom.

Feeling isolated or lonely
"I didn't want to let anyone know I was in menopause. It was definitely not information I had any desire to share with the rest of the world. Why would I? I'd only be leaving myself open to all kinds of stuff. I felt people would start to see me in a different way— that somehow they wouldn't see me as *me* anymore,

that they'd see 'menopause' or 'aging' or something.
So I kept what I was feeling to myself."

From a woman who experienced an early menopause:
"I knew *nobody* who'd been through menopause. I
was really *alone,* 'cause I didn't have anybody to talk
to. It was *alienating* to me to have that happen to
me in my 30s. . . . It's very clear to me that menopause
is a lonely experience. I've mentioned that I take
hormones to only two or three women—all women
about my age, contemporaries. And every one of them
has offered to give me herbal tea, or to tell me how
to get off them, or whatever. So, I don't tell anybody
anymore."

"They say there's about 25% [of women at menopause]
who have a really bad time. I fall into that group,
and I can assure you, there's no sympathy out there.
There was nobody to let me know that, look, it's okay,
you're not crazy. . . . I had a great deal of loneliness.
Al is a man, and men don't experience these changes.
They don't have a monthly period. They don't have
babies. And to try to gain an understanding there,
it's pretty hard."

The partners of women having a difficult time may
also feel isolated. As one woman said:

"He was all alone too 'cause there was nobody he
could talk to. What's he going to do, tell his buddy
his wife is picking on him all the time? That's not
very loyal and not very manly. He didn't say much.
My heart goes out to him. . . . It took me a year to

recover my marriage. There was a *lot* of damage done while I was in menopause."

With respect to menopause, it is perhaps those who have an early or difficult menopause who feel the most isolated. However, to varying degrees the other women felt isolated as well because many of us avoid talking about anything that might cause others to think of us as "menopausal."

Besides protecting us, keeping silent about what we are feeling can also separate us from potential sources of support, such as from those who have had similar experiences. And feeling cut off from others can seriously lower our self esteem.

When we don't know if other women feel the same way as we do we will often keep our experiences to ourselves. Otherwise, we can feel at risk of being thought of as sick or abnormal. So many of us keep silent when we have facial hair removed, take a tranquilizer, dye our hair, try to cover age spots or use a wig to cover hair loss. Yet when women feel safe from criticism or labelling, the most common expression I hear is, *"I thought I was the only one who felt that way!"*

In contrast, a lesbian who had always felt isolated because she'd never had children reported feeling *more* connected with other women. "Now that I'm in menopause, for the first time I feel identified with all women. I can share the same female talk [of menopause]." Now she shares infertility with her peers.

Feeling sad

"I burst into tears at the drop of a hat!"

"I had these *torrents* of sadness."

"Sad, sad, sad. I don't know why, but I do know that's how I feel. If I knew *why,* I wouldn't feel so crazy, and if I didn't feel so crazy I wouldn't feel so touchy, and if I didn't feel so touchy I'd be easier to live with, and if I was easier to live with I'd like myself a whole lot more!"

These women had children. Their sadness was not easily explained as being a desire for more children or having an "empty nest." We can't assume that wanting a child or having an empty nest is solely responsible for the heightened emotions many of us feel during menopause. The implication is that if we are busy enough, if life is full enough, menopause will not be an issue. As the experiences of the women quoted here suggest, this assumption is simplistic and ignores the many and often hidden sides of menopause.

For the women who wanted a child, but were unable to have one, menopause often triggered new levels of grief beyond that felt by the other women. Often, they felt they were losing their last chance to have a child.

Feeling relief

Menopause often brought relief for the women who had tried, unsuccessfully, to have a child. A long struggle had finally ended. At last, they were able to turn their attention to other parts of their lives. Any pressure they had felt to have a child was gone. And, as one woman said, "I don't feel less-than as a woman anymore."

On completion of menopause, those who had concerns about fibroids, endometriosis and migraines often found those concerns were lessened, if not removed. And some women were relieved to know they could no longer get pregnant. For others, relief came because they had, at last, moved out of the turbulence of "the change," and were now on more secure ground.

Feeling devalued

"Everybody that I talked to either hadn't had the experiences I was having or they looked at me as if I was a bit touched in the head. Or they'd imply that I didn't have anything *real* to complain about. I didn't feel as though anyone was *hearing* what I was saying—and *that* just about drove me crazy!"

"If I'm upset about something and my husband looks at the calendar or says, 'Are you taking your hormones right now?' then I could *really* kill him. It's like he's saying that what's bothering me isn't *real*. But there *is* something bothering me! If people stay calm and listen to me in the beginning, then I'm okay and I won't fly off the handle. If someone cracks a joke or pretends that it isn't actually happening, that's it! Once I get going I don't stop, until I've said everything I have to say. And I don't know any other way . . . .My husband says, *Why are you shouting?* And I say, *Do you hear me?* And he says, *Well, you said it five times!* And I say, *Well, you still haven't answered me!*"

"My husband gave me what I call pseudo-sympathy in that he did sympathize with me when I was having problems connected with menopause. But I often felt that he was looking at me with a jaundiced eye wondering why I just couldn't be stoic or not feel this way."

"I said to my doctor, 'I'm starting to notice my periods being more irregular than ever before. Do you think that could be menopause?' He said, 'no.' But of course it was, and right when I expected it."

It is not uncommon for many of us, regardless of our age, to feel we haven't been HEARD. This is one of the ways we, as women, most frequently feel devalued or patronized—be it at work, in a doctor's office or at home. Even those of us who are recognized for our strength or authority often experience not being listened to or taken seriously. In a landmark study, Mary Field Belenky and her colleagues noted how often women told them in anger and frustration how frequently they felt unheard and unheeded—both at home and at work.[5] So although not being heard is an experience familiar to many of us outside menopause, we often feel it more intensely amidst the complex dynamics of this transition.

Many of the women criticized articles they came across in women's magazines which suggested that they simply needed to exercise, improve their nutrition and lifestyles and develop a positive outlook in order to sail through menopause. They knew that this would help them have a more comfortable menopause and better health in general. However, they felt their menopause was being trivialized because how they were *actually feeling* was not being addressed. On the other hand, literature from the women's movement sometimes minimized menopause by focusing solely on socio-cultural factors and down-playing the impact of physical experiences.[6] The women wanted equal recognition for the impact on them of *all* aspects of their menopause: emotional, physical and social/cultural. And, in particular, they needed to understand how the interaction of all these aspects affected them.

Feeling embarrassed

Especially during the first half of their menopausal years, a strong thread running through most of the women's experiences is that *their* menopause was, somehow, embarrassing. Although the women who had hot flashes thought they *should not* be embarrassed by them, they usually were. A hot flash was an outward sign of what is going on inside: menopause.

"I have trouble telling people [about menopause]. I worry about what they might think. I mean, *I* had preconceptions about what 'menopausal' meant, and it meant getting old, so others most likely feel the same. If I tell somebody, 'I'm post-menopausal,' they're going to think I'm old. So, why would I tell somebody? It doesn't make sense. . . . I remember being in women's groups where it was discussed, and what I heard was, 'I'm *dreading* it.' But mostly we'd act like it's not happening! And we would talk about a *friend's* menopausal problems, but nobody in the group would say, *I'm* having problems too."

"With hot flashes I felt that I *looked* strange. I mean, I was *dripping*. And that was embarrassing."

"What I hear from my girl friends is, 'Oh, no, not me yet.'. . . . But when we're having problems with our kids we tell everybody in the world, and so do all our girl friends. Do you know what I mean? So [menopause is] a different type of a problem. . . . There's *shame* associated with it. And we think of it as *that* type rather than a *human* kind of problem."

"I didn't tell anyone how I was feeling at that time in my life—at least, not how I was feeling about being in menopause."

"I was embarrassed because I *felt* unfeminine and sexless, that I'd lost some worth, somehow—as a woman—and about getting older too."

"I'd get weepy, and I'd be so embarrassed. I'd go to a movie and there I'd be, tears coming down. And I couldn't control it!. . . . I can tell you that during that time [while in menopause] I became a person I did *not* like. I didn't like me at all."

"I don't tell anybody I'm taking hormones. I mean, I get very embarrassed. The whole thing feels so covert."

"My mind just goes blank, and I don't know why. Sometimes I can't even continue speaking because I forget what I'm talking about. And I'm a very articulate woman. Now, *that* is embarrassing!"

Those of us who have these experiences have them for a reason. And when we don't talk about them, there is also a good reason. What we keep silent—secret, hidden—remains protected. These women's statements show that there is something more than a straightforward biological process at work here. There is something about being afraid of how people will respond.

Feeling "out of control"
"I feel like I'm losing it these days." "I feel like my

body is falling apart." "I don't recognize myself anymore!" These feelings, however brief, can be very frightening. And, for many of us, they raise the specter of hysteria, of becoming the negative stereotype of the menopausal woman or of heading for a "nervous breakdown."

Our majority culture places a lot of value on being in control (in contrast to other cultures in the world which are more comfortable openly expressing a wide range of emotions and behavior). Here, we tend to feel embarrassed if we "lose control" of ourselves. Control is seen as being synonymous with power, dignity and mental health. And a lack of control is associated with weakness, inadequacy or mental instability. Our majority culture *assumes* that we need to control ourselves (our emotions and bodies), and that without control "all hell would break loose."

For most of us, the more insecure we feel, the greater our need for control. If we feel like we're losing control of ourselves, we usually try to hide it from others. We commonly think of personal "loss of control" as shameful and dangerous. These attitudes and concerns about control are not universal: they can and do vary from culture to culture.

Whenever we experience changes or emotions we do not understand, we can feel out of control. Both these conditions apply to many of our experiences of menopause within our majority culture. If we believe there is a problem with our bodies (hormones mis-behaving, an insufficient supply of estrogen, etc.) we can believe our bodies/ourselves are not as they should be. It is no wonder that so many of us report feeling out of control during menopause. Nor is it surprising if we find this alarming—so alarming, in fact, that many of us seek relief from this state in any way we can.

Feeling frustrated or angry

In the women I've worked with, anger about meno-pause came from two sources: anger while *in menopause,* and anger which came *as a result of talking about their experiences and hearing those of other women.* I'll discuss this second type of anger in a later chapter. Some of the *in-menopause* anger was a product of not having enough information or feeling dismissed, out of control, or labelled. Feeling strong anger close to the surface can be disconcerting—particularly for those of us who live in a culture which tells us that anger is not feminine.

Some of the women's anger related to feeling betrayed, an emotion we found difficult to understand at first. After exploring it, some of the women felt betrayed by their body because it was changing in ways they didn't understand. For others, it seemed more like they had been betrayed by other women who hadn't told them about how menopause had affected them emotionally and physically. Others felt betrayed by researchers and the medical community who didn't have answers to their questions—who asked them to make decisions about hormone therapy without adequate or agreed-upon information.

Feeling afraid

"When I was around 45, I started bleeding very heavily, and that was very frightening for me. Sometimes I was afraid to go out on the second day of my periods because there would be floods of stuff."

"Becoming infertile was somehow tied in with a vague fear about losing my existing children. And I don't know why."

[From a woman with an early menopause] "At home, it was frightening how fast I could get upset. And I mean *really* upset. . . .my body would be trembling . . . .When I say I know I'm not crazy, I *didn't* know, then. I was really afraid, because my mother had been very loving, playful, and I adored her. And then she got *strange*. . . .and [would] just scream at me. . . .I guess for years I had a nagging fear that I would go that way. For the first time, I've been thinking about how old she was at that time. She was 36, about my age. It just breaks my heart to think that it might have been the menopause with her and she didn't know and I didn't know."

"I can remember truly wondering whether I was going out of my mind. That's because I didn't know I was in menopause. I hadn't even thought about it. And it's very, very frightening to have those tremendous [emotional] ups and downs. . . .I didn't recognize myself. I felt like I became this ugly person who had no control over herself."

Fear is a natural outcome of many of the common themes discussed so far. When we do not understand or feel comfortable with our emotions or body changes—and how the two interact—we can expect fear. And, quite naturally, the women feared the unknown. This related to the general lack of adequate information—particularly about the possible health hazards which are now being associated with menopause. And many of the women also had very real concerns about their future as post-menopausal, aging women in this society.

Anger can serve as a protection from fear. It can be a way to keep fear at bay or to generate enough energy to combat it. Anger can be a way of looking after ourselves in the face of fear. And, conversely, for women in particular, fear often accompanies anger or rage: for example, fear of reprisals, of losing love or of being seen as unfeminine. Many of us are afraid of what expressing anger will do to our relationships. In part, this fear during menopause can relate to not understanding where these emotions come from. "Am I losing my mind?" "I'm afraid these raging hormones are going to destroy my marriage." "Is my partner still going to find me desirable when I'm dripping in sweat?" "Am I going to lose my desire for sex?" These fears can feel like a very real threat to our intimate relationships.

"What's 'Real' and What's 'Hormonal'?"

This is a question I have heard many women ask so I use it here. By doing so I am not implying that anything hormonally-based is not "real." In fact, as I hope I make clear throughout this book, I believe our menopausal experience is an interaction between our inner and outer world.

Many women in the groups found themselves in a "validity dilemma" around their emotions during menopause. In their words, they were trying to sort out whether what they were feeling was "hormonally related" or not. While they expressed this in many different ways, they were essentially asking themselves, "Is this emotion caused or magnified by my hormones or am I having a straight-forward response to the situation I'm in? Is the source of the problem located inside me or outside of me?" As demonstrated over and over throughout this book, there is a tendency in our mainstream culture to assume that when we not understand why we (or other women) are feeling the way we do, there must be a problem with our hormones. And this makes sense on several levels. We haven't been recognizing the influence of the emotional and social-cultural sides of menopause and we have focused mostly on the physical. Therefore, when it is not clear to us why our emotions are magnified, it is natural to assume the cause is physical: a hormonal imbalance. Yet, when we look below the surface, we discover many other possible non-physical explanations for these emotions.

For example, most of the women reported situations similar to the one this woman describes: "When I'm angry, my anger feels more 'legitimate' if I *know* the reason for it is outside of myself, such as something someone said or did which deserves my anger. But my anger feels less valid to me—and to everyone else— when we all believe it is caused by my hormones. Then, I usually feel guilty as well, because there seems to be something wrong with me which is creating a problem for others."

This "validity" dilemma occurred most often when the women were sad, angry, or in conflict with someone. They doubted themselves more than usual, asking themselves whether they had a *right* to be sad, to be angry or whether they were being fair.

"It frustrated me that the *realness* of my feelings was in doubt. Yet, what could I say? I knew I wasn't a very likeable person then. I *wasn't*. I had no barriers to saying anything. I'd just roar it out anyway. . . . I felt so many frustrations, like: Is this really fair that I'm blamed in this way [hearing that I was acting 'menopausal' or that my hormones were out of control]?....My *patience* ran out!....I became this person I didn't know, and behaved in ways that I didn't understand....I just wasn't used to this person."

"During that time [early years of menopause] I *couldn't sort out* what was really bothering me. Was it hormones or not? I was so frustrated and angry! And I'd never know if it was valid or not. I found it very confusing. What's a valid complaint and what isn't? In all fairness, there were times when I was hysterical, and I would prefer that he didn't take it all that seriously. But it's certainly annoying to have been so upset and to have it brushed off as hormonal. It's *terrible.* It's a tough one....I think one of the *hardest* parts of menopause for me was making the distinctions: am I really upset or am I under the influence of hormones?"

What is significant here is that it is natural for us to be concerned about being labelled "hysterical" or "menopausal." Real and important emotions and issues are too often brushed aside when these terms are applied to us. Anxiety over being thought of as hysterical and menopausal can naturally add to any confusion and uncertainty we may be feeling.

Of course, adding to this dilemma is the fact that how hormones affect emotions and how emotions affect hormones is not fully understood. This is a version of the classic question: Which came first, the chicken or the egg? Nor is the interrelationship between our health and the physical, social, cultural and spiritual sides of ourselves fully understood. In our majority culture, we are only beginning to ask these questions and as yet there are no clear, agreed-upon answers.

However, on exploration, we can find external causes for the women's emotions during menopause, natural reactions to societal and cultural meanings associated with menopause and aging. This does not mean that hormonal fluctuations are not involved; but it does mean that in addition to asking how our hormones affect our emotions, we need to be asking how our inner and outer worlds interact.

To fully understand menopause, we need to recognize all the sides of menopause and their interactions.

4
Menopause Means I'm No Longer Young

Becouse our bodies are in constant change, where we begin to call this change "aging" is somewhat arbitrary.[7] It can vary from one culture to another, as well as from one historical period to another.

"With menopause age had all-of-a-sudden come to me."

"It was a real recognition that time moves on and now I was an older woman."

"For me, menopause *meant* I was aging, and aging was a problem for me."

One of the strongest common themes for the women was that being in menopause was a signal of the end of youth. While that door had been closing for some time, menopause meant it had shut. *Despite differences in their chronological age, menopause had this meaning for all the women.* As one woman in menopause in her 30's, said: "It meant I was never going to be a young woman again." From another in her late 20's: "Intellectually, I know I'm still a young woman. But I *feel* as though I've lost a good portion of my youth. Not just not being able to have children, but my *youth*. And no one around me seems to understand that!" With menopause coming so early, these women go through a level of grief which far exceeds that of other women who feel their menopause is more-or-less on time.

When menopause acts as a signal of the end of youth—that is, as a signal of aging—it becomes important to understand what aging means to women. Rita Freedman in her book, *Beauty Bound,* writes that, in terms of aging, those of us in the majority culture are dealing with more than wrinkles and grey hair. We are also faced with a set of sobering statistics describing reality for aging females:

"Aging women are the fastest growing poverty group in this country. Females comprise nearly three quarters of the elderly poor, and their impoverished state is often linked with being unmarried. There are three times as many single women as single men over age fifty. Four out of five elderly women live alone. In one third of the second marriages the bride is more than a decade younger than the groom, and she can expect to live the last ten years of her life as an aged, often poor widow."[8]

Susan Sontag coined the phrase, "the double standard of aging" to describe the greater *acceptability* of aging in men versus aging in women.[9] Men may have their own difficulties in aging, but, as Elissa Melamed in her book, *Mirror, Mirror: The Terror of Not Being Young,* explains, as women, we have a different emotional and social experience:

"There is a sex-linked imbalance in traditional portrayals of the old. We find many positive portraits of older men—but virtually none of older women. And the most negative age-linked archetype of all is always female: the witch....the only truly powerful symbol of older womankind we inherit....Sometimes she is wise and benevolent, but generally not....There is no male counterpart to the witch or hag with her ugly features, warts, scrawny bones, and hanging flesh—nor any male figure who rivals the horror and loathing she inspires. She....[embodies] our fear of aging."[10]

With menopause signalling this possible future, many of us will naturally have very mixed emotions about the "change of life." Grieving the loss of youth becomes far more than a narcissistic exercise given the enormous value the mainstream culture places on youth. This rather dour picture will change only when we expand our standards of femininity and sexual attractiveness so that they include those of us beyond our fertile/youthful years.

There is a commonly held belief that, because we live longer now, we were never meant to go through menopause. Margaret Lock, an anthropologist who has extensively researched menopause, responds to this belief in a letter to the editor in *Healthsharing* magazine:

"This commonly held belief is incorrect. The average life expectancy was much lower two centuries ago, but this was due to high infant mortality and to the fact that many women died in childbirth. Those who survived to the age of 40 had an extremely good chance of going on to reach an old age of 65 years or more.

A good number of old people have existed since classical times at least. Suggesting that menopause is a 'recent' phenomenon is not only erroneous but dangerous, because it allows certain interested parties to promote the idea that post-menopausal women are 'unnatural' and therefore that they must be medicated, otherwise they are very likely to disintegrate."[11]

Lock discusses these ideas further in her book, *Encounters with Aging: Mythologies of Menopause in Japan and North America* (University of California Press, Berkeley, CA).

Another popular belief is that it is important to separate menopause from midlife or aging. This too must be re-examined. Most well-known theories of development and aging have been based on the experiences of men, and men do not go through menopause. As a result, we have become accustomed to discussing menopause as though it were separate from the process of mid-life/aging. For the majority of us, midlife *means* menopause: they go hand in hand. With the exception of women who have an early menopause, there is no such thing as midlife without menopause. Midlife and aging for women are vastly different from midlife and aging in men.

For women, midlife and aging must be studied and discussed as interconnected with the physical and emotional aspects of menopause. Unless we think of them as interconnected we perpetuate the idea that we are separate from our bodies and that the way we experience menopause can be separated from the rest of our lives.

When we discuss ourselves as women, as compared to other women, without comparing ourselves to men, how can we separate menopause from aging? The commonly-heard question, "Is it menopause or simply aging?" ignores the emotional and social differences in the experiences of aging in men and women.

Unlike men, women leave fertility behind at midlife. Men, on the other hand, remain fertile much longer. For us, youth and fertility go hand in hand. The two are equated for women but not for men. A man can father a child in elder years, whereas women cannot conceive after menopause. Therefore, because menopause serves as a signal for the end of fertility, it also signals the end of youth. Men have no such clear marker in their aging process.

Yes, there are similarities in the aging of men and women: tone and texture changes in the skin, possible weight gain, changes in levels of sexual interest and grey hair are a few. The differences—covering the biological, psychological, social and cultural—are, however, much more profound. They are at the core of majority culture ideas about what is *most* valuable in women. Even the similarities of male and female aging are experienced differently because they will naturally have different meanings for us than for men. In our mainstream culture, a change, for example, in skin tone or texture often has a far greater significance in the life of a woman than of a man. And as long as our *majority culture* continues to value "youthful" skin tone and texture and equate it to a woman's "value"—*something it does not do with men*—aging and its signals will always be a profoundly different experience for us as women.

Imagine a husband proudly announcing to friends,

''Hey, my wife's in menopause!''

much as he might have announced her pregnancy.

5
I Don't Want To Be Labelled 'Menopausal'

The stereotype of the menopausal woman is of a woman who appears to be overly emotional, angry or depressed. At one time or another, many of us in menopause do feel just like this stereotype. So labeling a woman "menopausal" is not like describing her as "tall." Nor does it have the same value as describing her as "pregnant" or "married." Because of this lack of value and because of the negative stereotype, calling a woman "menopausal" is not a compliment in our majority culture. As a result, menopause remains tangled in attitudes that can make it difficult for many of us to admit to what we are actually feeling during menopause or to discuss it. A *desire to avoid this label* played a central role in the women's experiences of menopause.

* * * * * * * * *

Most of us in the majority culture are aware of the stereotype of the menopausal woman before we begin menopause. And it is common for us to feel insulted if someone suggests we are in menopause when we are not. The women I've worked with were no exception. Before menopause, many of them had thought of women in menopause as aging, matronly, dry, lacking vitality and colorless:

"Middle aged, not attractive, not pleasant, angry, giving someone hell."

"Unpredictable, ... menopausal women get strange. I mean, I think that's the biggest one."

"Not able to control herself. And I *couldn't* a lot of the time!"

"Red-faced, sweating. The butt of jokes."

"Shrewish, overly emotional."

But the women were seldom aware of the *power* of this stereotype until they were actually *in* menopause. Only then did they feel its effects.

"My family had a tendency to discount what I was saying as well as my emotions, especially if I was angry. They'd attribute it to my being in menopause. It was as though they were saying themselves, 'She's menopausal. Don't pay any attention to her.'"

"I didn't want people to know I was in menopause. It felt negative. Looking back, I was protecting myself."

"It's like, if I'm being 'menopausal' have I stopped being a woman? I feel as though I am in this non-state: not a womanly woman or a *'real'* woman, but not man. Hell, I don't know who I am!"

"Irrational. . . .The stereotype was true for me, about the irrational part. Fair enough. What's offensive about it, though, is the condescending nature of it. . . .You know, the *not* listening, and not really knowing how it is for the woman from the inside out. . . .That stereotype made it harder for me. It still makes it hard for me because, like I say, I don't tell people that I'm on hormone therapy."

"When he thought my behavior was irrational, my husband's first thought was menopause. He picked up on the stereotype of the hysterical woman at menopause."

We have here the image of women who might be thought of as "losing it." In fact, the comments of younger women, men, and much of the medical literature are filled with references to the stereotypical menopausal woman as having lost control.[12]

In our dominant culture we have all manner of stereotypes. Some of the stereotypes that affect women the most are those of beauty, femininity, the nature of a "Womanly woman," of a good mother, and of how we should age. We learn about these stereotypes in childhood and adolescence and we rarely question them. Most of us must constantly deal with the difference between these stereotypes and our own lives, bodies and experiences because such ideals are impossible to meet and bear little relation to our actual lives. We are surrounded by images of the ideal body shape, ideal wife, ideal mother and ideal career woman. Although few of us know anyone who has actually reached all these standards, most of us see them as goals to struggle toward.

The flip side of these ideals is a negative stereotype—such as those of the "unfeminine woman," the "ugly woman," the "bitch," the "bad mother," the "domineering woman," the "controlling woman," and the woman who is not "aging gracefully." We tend to work hard at avoiding any association with these descriptions. And we can feel shame when we suspect we are actually *being* one of these women. Yet we can't help but find ourselves becoming disturbingly close to these negative stereotypes quite frequently—because the reality is that most of us will never reach these popular ideals of beauty and femininity.

Stereotypes do serve a purpose, at times. For example, they can help us to put our world into order. The stereotype of what appeals to men will simplify my search for a suitable gift when I pull the name of a man I hardly know for the office Christmas gift exchange. I can be relatively safe passing by flowing scarves, perfume and lingerie. The disadvantages of stereotypes, however, tend to outweigh the advantages. When we stereotype someone, we label her in some way. Then we risk losing sight of the person behind the label. Making assumptions about a "type" of person hides her behind the label and renders her individuality "invisible."

As a negative stereotype, the "menopausal woman" has been around for a long time. Despite many changes in the lives of women in the majority culture, this stereotype still has a lot of power. We have good reason to be afraid of being seen as sweaty, distraught, angry or "too emotional" because this portrays us as being about as far from the ideal of femininity and desirability as we can get.

When we feel embarrassment and shame it is a signal that we believe we have been negatively judged. What judgment is more negative than that of a damning stereotype? It's not even *personalized*. And it is not unusual to feel uncertain about why we're embarrassed—because stereotypes are often internalized at an early age, so they can seem like something that ought to be. Such situations are common throughout our lives. For example, body odor, facial hair or a strong display of anger all relate to the stereotype of the unfeminine woman. And many, if not most, of us feel some embarrassment or shame when we think we "smell," grow facial hair, or get "too emotional,"—because we've crossed over into "unfeminine" land.

A now-discontinued advertisement in a medical journal for prescription estrogen provides an example of this stereotype: an obviously complaining, shrewish, hysterical woman is portrayed as preventing a calm and reasonable man from driving the bus in which she rides. The caption reads, "He is suffering from estrogen deficiency; she is the reason why." Like all stereotypes, this one contains just enough truth to make it uncomfortable. Many of us do, in fact, periodically *feel* this way during menopause. The damning label here is "menopausal" or "estrogen deficient." It is a description most of us would naturally try to avoid through whatever socially-acceptable means available to us. To date, the most viable of these socially-acceptable means have been either silence or medication.

As women, many of us may intuitively choose to keep silent about some of our deeper feelings in order to protect ourselves from being labelled "menopausal."[13]

And when no one knows how we actually feel, the resulting sense of invisibility can be one of the most profoundly disturbing of human experiences. When Ayla in *Clan of the Cave Bear* is ostracized by her clan she experiences a profound trauma because she is treated as if she no longer exists. Our very identity can be threatened when we don't feel seen or acknowledged. And when others label us in a negative way, we usually feel devalued as a person. Instinctively, we try to protect ourselves from these dangers—like the child from another country who becomes "the silent type" to avoid being teased for her accent.

It is understandable that much of menopause still remains in the closet because most of us will naturally keep quiet in order not to be labelled and stereotyped. Until menopause has at least the same value to us— and to men—as being young, being pregnant or having a partner, many of us will choose to keep to ourselves some or most of our experiences of menopause. Whenever we sense that what we are going through is not valued or understood by others, a natural response is protect ourselves from being judged, devalued or misunderstood by remaining silent.

6

A Connection Between Beginnings and Endings: Menstruation and Menopause

Another experience common to the women in the groups was that menarche (the beginning of menstruation) and menopause (the ending of menstruation) were more than physically connected. They found that cultural attitudes toward one also influenced the other.

Their experiences reveal a picture of menopause very much influenced by a menstrual taboo. A *taboo* is what a culture considers forbidden, shameful or best kept quiet and out of sight. And a taboo often gives birth to a negative stereotype. Whatever our culture, its taboos may be difficult for us to see, let alone discuss, because they are deeply ingrained in our society and become internalized early in life as a part of our process of growing up. Often they become an accepted part of our lives and, consequently, they are rarely questioned. Alice Miller, well known for her work in relation to taboos, notes that any one generation finds it difficult to see its own taboos—like the fish trying to see the water in which it swims.[14]

Menstruation, and our majority culture's attitude toward it, is something all of us share. Our first menstruation not only heralds fertility, but also lays a foundation for the ending of fertility. With a natural menopause, our usually lengthy history of menstruating winds down. And our menstrual history plays a significant role in how we go through this transition.

Paula Weideger, in her landmark book, *Menstruation and Menopause: The Physiology and Psychology, the Myth and the Reality*, writes:

"It is obvious that menopause has a physiological connection to the menstrual cycle (there can be no ending without a beginning—the mechanisms which underlie the former also control the latter). But it has been far less obvious that the ways in which we think about menopause and even the manner in which it is experienced are, emotionally and socially, legacies of the taboo of menstruation. The image of what menopause might be, the anxiety or even horror with which it may be anticipated, are placed upon a woman from the moment she begins to menstruate."[15]

There is a school of thought which suggests that menstruation and menopause are merely biological events, and to say more is to make too much of a small thing.[16] Nothing could be further from the truth. "The ramifications of the cycle of female sex hormone production take us beyond the realm of the biochemical and physiological. Menstruation and menopause are part of our emotional and social experience as well."[17]

The women in the groups made these comments on beginning to menstruate:

"I was really pleased [to begin to menstruate because] it meant to me that I was normal. . . . 'Cause I wasn't sure, at that time, at that age. When I was growing up they were still selling Kotex in boxes covered with brown paper. It was just something you didn't talk about very much. . . .The impression I had was this was kind of secret and not so very nice."

"It was almost a non-event. . . . It was a very great inconvenience though. . . . I didn't want anybody to know [when I was menstruating]."

"I didn't experience much trouble with my periods . . . . My mother told me, 'You're going to have this thing happen to you and then you're going to become a woman.' She was very embarrassed doing it, and I picked up on that. I felt uncomfortable. . . . I *needed* privacy during that time, [to] not let people know."

"It meant a lot more messy involvement with my body. I mean, I didn't have to pay attention to it before I started menstruating. Then suddenly, once a month, there was all this mess and fuss and discomfort."

"I always worried about showing. I was terrified of the possible embarrassment of it all. Afraid of blood running down my legs or seeping through my clothes, or of my pad falling out in the middle of the hallway."

"From the beginning, I got the message that I should

be very careful about keeping all signs of menstruating out of sight, especially from my father and brothers."

"The first time was very scary. And I went from running and jumping and being carefree to having to be more careful. My family told me having my periods was special but it didn't *feel* special to me!"

"I didn't like it very much because it was an uncomfortable thing....It was kept deadly secret....I was afraid of odor. ....I remember a sense of shame."

"The first time, and since, didn't really mean anything to me. I've always tried not to think about it, not to make a big deal out of it."

They talk about menstruation being unimportant, best kept out of sight and embarrassing. They talk of feeling anxious about public humiliation. This echos what they said about menopause. These are *not* responses to a straight-forward biological event. Instead, they reflect deeply-ingrained cultural attitudes and values about both menstruation and menopause.

Our experiences of menstruation vary as much as our experiences of menopause. Each of us is influenced by our personal history, especially by our family's attitudes toward women, their bodies and reproductive processes. And we are powerfully influenced by the dominant culture. Television, films, advertisements, magazines, the education system, the medical community, popular literature, myths and folk tales all convey our cultural values and attitudes. For example, despite the large number of sanitary napkin ads on television and in magazines, most girls in the majority culture are still taught to hide all signs of menstruation—particularly from males. (It is interesting that such ads have only recently been allowed on television in Britain.) Pressure to hide the evidence is a common thread running through most North American women's experiences of menstruation and menopause.

Diane Barthel, in her book *Putting On Appearances*, looks at today's advertisements for menstrual products. She points out that the images in these ads are not of fertility and power. Instead, they are about the severe limits placed on us as girls and women *unless* our menstruation is hidden and thereby controlled. The "curse" is now wiped from view, freeing us to participate in the modern age. In our majority culture we have the promise that absolutely no notice whatsoever will be given to the menstruating woman.

> "Her menses must be invisible; when it becomes visible, control has failed. She has had an 'accident.' The focus of advertisements is on cleanliness, purity, keeping menstruation hidden from public view and 'freedom' from the 'problems' associated with being female. These products are sold on their ability to keep menstruation a secret. Menstruation is viewed as a 'personal *problem*' that must be dealt with *individually*."[18]

Our first menstruation introduces us to the taboos and restrictions surrounding menstruation. It is then that most of us begin to receive subtle, confusing and usually nonverbal messages. On the one hand, we learn that menstruation is important because it means we are becoming a women, and because of its underlying tie to fertility, to the awesome power to conceive, to carry life within our bodies, and to give birth. On the other hand, we also receive messages of shame and secrecy for the *process responsible* for that fertility, menstruation.[19] This contradictory message provides the foundation on which most of our subsequent experiences of our bodies are built. In the majority culture, we are taught to value the idea and the outcome of fertility, but not the workings of the body on which that fertility depends. And, "when we are taught that something has to be hidden, we naturally believe that it contains an element that is not acceptable to other people."[20]

Without being aware of it, many of us have inherited beliefs that menstruation and menopause should not play a significant role in our lives. As Paula Weideger writes, "the denial of menstrual and menopausal realities, whether by women or by men, is part of the taboo of menstruation."[21] She adds:

"[Many primitive cultures] had the benefit of *knowing* that their community believed they were unclean. In our culture, where the rules of taboo are not articulated and there is little information about the positive experiences of menstruation and menopause, confusion and difficulty are bound to prevail. Instead of protesting the contemporary version of the taboo, women, unaware of its existence, protest the 'problem' of menstruation and its legacy, menopause."[22]

The menstrual taboo shapes our attitudes and values and leaves few of us unaffected. And, unfortunately, medical practitioners and researchers share the taboos of the society to which they belong. As Jane Ussher notes in, *The Psychology of the Female Body,* "considering the fact that half the world's population menstruates for a significant proportion of its life, there is very little discussion of it, either in literature or in more theoretical or academic writings."[23] And when we think of "feminine" as clean, sweet-smelling and gentle, the blood, smell and moods of menstruation can easily be seen as problems. It is interesting to speculate how differently we would feel about menstruating if men menstruated. I suspect it would then be highly valued, if not celebrated each month.

Now that "premenstrual syndrome" (PMS) has a medical definition, many of us now feel more able to talk about feelings associated with our periods. The danger here, as with menopause, is that the focus remains on *individual* women and on our bodies as the problem—rather than considering what influence social and cultural values might have on how we are feeling. The definition of a "syndrome" is a set of *symptoms* that together characterize a *disease* or a *disorder.* It's a short step from here to calling menstrual or menopausal complaints a disease.

A further example of this taboo is the number of boys who, when asked what they would dislike most about being a girl, say, "having periods." This is not surprising given the number of us who think of menstruation as, at best, an inconvenience, and at worse as a debilitating illness which strikes once a month. Mood swings and depression are now considered normal before menstruation. And there is a popular conception that women have more accidents, are more prone to suicide, more likely to commit crimes, and are less efficient and more irrational before or during menstruation.[24]

The way in which so many of us have absorbed and accepted the crippling view of the majority culture is clearly expressed by Paula Weideger quoting from a study which found that:

"most of the women [in the study] considered menstruation a biological liability and believed that men are in a superior position because they have a more advantageous (i.e. superior) biological makeup. . . .The menstrual taboo has influenced every thought and every feeling about menstruation, menopause, and being a woman."[25]

7

What Happens When We Separate Our *Selves* From Our *Bodies*?

While listening to the women's experiences, it became obvious that most of them spoke as if their menopause were either happening to someone else or was separate from their *Self*. For example, they would rarely say "my" menopause. Instead, they used "it" or "the." "It wouldn't let me go." "I felt as though I was being held prisoner by my body, and I wanted *out*." "What's me and what's menopause?" "I didn't know what my body was doing to me." From these words comes a sense of being "done to" by something outside themselves: their bodies.

As women in the majority culture, we "have inherited the beliefs that menstruation and menopause are not really a part of a woman's life and that the feelings stemming from either state are not as real as our other feelings."[26] Many of us have become accustomed to believing we are not our "real" selves during or before menstruation. This belief lays the foundation for our experience of menopause. And in the majority culture there is a certain value placed on us *not* paying attention to our periods: many of us speak as if what we are experiencing on a monthly basis is not happening to *us,* or, if it is sufficiently noticeable that it cannot be ignored, we say we are not ourselves. Our mainstream society *expects* us to ignore our periods in either of these two ways. This same society also expects us to do the same with menopause.

Emily Martin, in her book, *The Woman in the Body: A Cultural Analysis of Reproduction,* also found a tendency for women to speak as if their menopause were separate from themselves. She found the following to be some of the central beliefs reflected in their comments:

-Your body is something the "real" you has to adjust to or cope with
-Women who experience menstrual and/or meno-pausal discomfort feel at odds with the body they must "cope" with
-Your body needs to be controlled by your self
-Menstruation, menopause, labor, birthing and their various stages are states you go through or experiences that happen to you—not actions you *do* or an experience in which you actively *participate.*

These ways of seeing and thinking about our bodies are cultural in origin. They are not universal truths because not all cultures have these views. Chinese, Japanese, East Indian and North American Native cultures, to name a few, have a history of seeing a person as a whole—as an interconnected physical, emotional, social and spiritual being who is influenced by her environment. From this view, physical change will naturally influence us emotionally, socially and spiritually and vice versa.

Where does the idea of a split between mind and body originate? Morris Berman (among many others), in exploring the origins of current popular views of ourselves and of our relation to our world, notes that up to the 16th century mind and body were not viewed as particularly distinct from each other. *And consciousness resided in the body as well as in the mind.*

The assumption that mind and body were basically separate took shape during the scientific revolution of the 17th century when our ability to think was seen by Descartes to separate us from nature: "I think, therefore I am." As we were seen to be separate from nature, we were also seen to be separate from our bodies. Thinking came to be valued above other human activities such as laboring, crafting or intuiting. And the location of our thought processes, the mind, came to be seen as the location of our consciousness. Within the majority culture today, we still live with the outcome of this perspective. Although aware of our body and its functions, most of us think of our sense of Self, our "I," our consciousness, as residing in our mind—not in, or including, our body. This separation of mind ("ourselves") and body has become accepted as natural.

From the time of ancient Greece until the late 18th century, medical literature reflected the view that every part of the body was related to every other part. The body was seen as a system which had to stay in balance to remain healthy. Changes were seen to occur constantly throughout the lifespan and at some times more quickly or noticeably than at others. Our bodies were seen as continuously developing throughout our lives. Therefore, we (our bodies) were constantly in the process of re-balancing to adapt to changes throughout our lives; for example, during menstruation and during menopause.

When the Industrial Revolution came along, this long-established way of thinking about the body came under severe attack. Medical literature, in particular, began describing the body in terms of a factory. Then the body's functions and processes became thought of and talked about in economic and production-related terms. This view continues today: our medical literature is filled with words and ideas relating to performance, gains, losses, deficiencies and efficiency. Like a factory, parts are replaced, and the goal is to keep the factory operating efficiently. But "efficiently" here means *according to this view of the body and how it functions. From this perspective, the mind and consciousness are separate from the body, and parts of the body are separate from each other— just as a generator is separate from a conveyor belt.*

As Emily Martin notes in *The Woman in the Body,* many elements of modern medical science contribute to a fragmentation of us as persons:

"When science treats the person as a machine and assumes the body can be fixed by mechanical manipu-lations, it ignores, and it encourages us to ignore other aspects of our selves, such as our emotions or our relations with other people. Recent technological developments have allowed this tendency to progress very far. Parts of our bodies can now be moved from person to person; their purchase and sale can even be contemplated. The body as a machine without a mind or soul has become almost familiar."[27]

The full implication of such a conception of ourselves has barely begun to be explored. That this concept might exact a high price would not be surprising.

Women in the majority culture, in particular, are vulnerable to feeling this separation of Self from body. It may be that many of us make this separation to keep ourselves from being defined, valued and judged by our bodies. If we perceive something to be unacceptable, undesirable, unlovable or ugly a natural response could be to separate ourselves from it—*even if it is our own body.* From advertising and literature, as well as medical views of our bodies, we receive powerful and consistent messages that, as is, our bodies are not okay. In order to feel good about ourselves, many of us feel the need to fix or to ignore our "imperfect" bodies.

When a girl begins to menstruate—that is, when she is beginning to become fertile—we say that she is starting to become a woman. What, then, does ending menstruation mean?

8
I Don't Miss My Periods; I Don't Want More Children: Why Do I Feel Sad?

There seems to be a general fear that if we talk about the losses we may feel as a result of menopause we run the risk of developing physical or psychological problems. Even if this were true, and I don't believe it is, the risk of *not* talking about losses may be too great. As Alice Miller points out, "something one cannot talk about also cannot be buried, finds no resting place. If one doesn't refer to it, the wounds continue to fester from generation to generation."[28] What we do not name retains the power to shame us, to isolate us from each other and to keep us vulnerable. When we can identify our losses—what we are leaving—we are more able to let them go in peace. We then increase the possibilities in what we are moving toward.

Menopause clearly brought losses for the women I worked with. To return to the analogy of an onion, it was here that the women found themselves at the deeper layers. These were the less visible and more difficult-to-discuss aspects of their experience. They struggled to find the words to describe their feelings and determine what caused them. This difficulty is not surprising given the long history of silence around menopause.

Choosing silence about our deepest feelings may be a way that many of us intuitively use to protect ourselves from labels such as those still surrounding menopause. For the women, this history of silence got in the way when they tried to sort out their emotions. In a sense, they were trying to talk about subjects taboo even to themselves. And their efforts were complicated because they were angry or sad that menopause was not generally valued by society and that, therefore, the losses seemed to out-weigh the gains. Intuitively, they felt that this should not be so. Adding to their discomfort was the suspicion that they were not quite measuring up as liberated women. Nonetheless, "shoulds" aside, menopause brought with it a number of losses—some large and some.

The most obvious menopause-related change for the women was that they were no longer menstruating. Over the years of menopause their cycles became irregular and gradually stopped. On the surface this felt more like a gain than a loss. They were clearly happy to leave menstrual inconveniences behind. Gone was the potential for embarrassment which went along with menstruation. They were happy to be done with pads, tampons, and the need to have *sanitary* supplies on hand. What was missing, however, was a visible cycle which had been an important part of their lives for 30 - 40 years. Whether seen as "my friend" or "the curse," a familiar pattern and marker-of-time connected to their womanhood had ended.

Under the Surface of Fertility

As it turns out, none of the women having a menopause "on time" wanted more children. "The thought of having a child *at my age* is just horrible to me! So how come I feel as though I've lost something?" "Why do I feel sad if I don't care if I'm fertile anymore?" As they had all the children they wanted, why did it matter that they were unable to have more? "I've had a tubal ligation. I'm already infertile, so being sad doesn't make sense." This paradox made them feel as though they were swimming upstream against the force of logic.

Individually, they tended to doubt themselves and often felt dangerously close to the stereotype of the menopausal woman. "I didn't want to sound crazy." "I thought I was the only one who felt that way." "I thought it had to be my hormones because how I was feeling didn't make sense." However, being in a nonjudgemental group empowered women to explore beyond the stereotype and to look for the source of what seemed to them to be irrational feelings. By giving their emotions credibility they were able to uncover the source of their emotions and discover what meanings menopause had for them.

What was important was what fertility *ultimately* meant to them. This meaning was far more complex than simply the ability to bear children or to menstruate. Because menopause ended fertility (either in actuality or, if they were infertile earlier, symbolically), it had implications and associations which related to how they felt about themselves as feminine, valued, sexual women. Here the women were in territory most often hidden even from themselves, and visible only when reassured by the experiences of other women that they weren't neurotic or unusual.

"There was just this tremendous fear that *without* that ability, that reproductive ability, I was nothing, as a woman. You know? *That's* what was terrifying, that I was *losing* something awfully important, and I might not have anything left at the end."

"A tubal ligation felt like an effective form of birth control, not nonfertility."

"There was sadness involved because I realized I was no longer ever going to be fertile again, although I'd already had my tubes tied." [Note: it may be that the association of menstruation with fertility is too ingrained in women's psyches to be removed by the historically-recent advent of tubal ligations. As long as a woman continues to menstruate, on some deep level she may continue to think of herself as fertile.]

"Now I don't feel the loss so much, but in the beginning I was afraid I'd lost all my feminine hormones and that I didn't look feminine anymore. I started feeling like I wasn't a real woman anymore."

"I felt sexless, absolutely sexless, and *un*feminine and that was one of the biggest reasons for my sadness, and why I felt like a *nil*."

"The sorrow and confusion I felt related to being a full-bodied woman and to losing some femininity during menopause. On a scale of one to 10, I feel as though I went into menopause as a nine, and came out a six or a seven as a Woman, capital W."

These are the words of emotionally and physically healthy women who are actively involved in both nontraditional and traditional female roles. Yet, they felt that menopause brought a loss of something important related to their sense of themselves as women. What was crucial was that nothing of *equal value* in the *same woman-realm* replaced this loss. Why should this be so, given that menopause is a natural experience shared by all of us? The answer can be found in our majority culture history and present-day society.

Messages About Fertility and Value

In Western European/North American societies, value *as a woman* has been *most* associated with our ability to bear children and with our sexual availability. Within this heritage, *menstruation and fertility define us as women.* There is an ordinariness to this statement—it's almost like stating the obvious. The sense of normality here stems from the biological truth that menstruation and the ability to bear children do, in fact, *distinguish* the two sexes, women from men.

However, males have tended to serve as this culture's standard and model of humanness.[29] Because male experiences, bodies and thoughts have been taken to be the norm, as women we easily became *defined* by the ways in which we most significantly *differ from* men: menstruation and the ability to give birth. So, within our dominant culture, what it means to be a woman has become narrowly defined through comparison to men. As a result, what is *most valued* in us, *as women*, became *restricted* to the ways in which we most obviously *differed* from men: menstruation and the ability to bear children.

In contrast, in a society in which the sexes are different-yet-equal, one sex cannot, by definition, serve as a standard for the other as each is unique, a standard unto itself.

The practice of defining us by the ways in which we differ from men can be traced back through history. (A more thorough exploration of these concepts is provided in works such as those of Berman, Martin, Rich, Weideger, among others.) Even today, what generally remains most highly valued in us, as women, is our sexuality and reproductive capacity—that is, our bodies—not our minds, our actions or even a balance between all three.

An advertising billboard contains one word, "Femininity," and one image, that of a young woman's firm torso. Another recent advertisement suggests, "You know what's really important." In it, a man pulls back the bodice of a woman's dress, looking at her breasts. Both these advertisements link femininity with a woman's body and sexual availability. Advertisements, movies, television, magazines, novels, even textbooks, continue to transmit powerful messages about what to value in females. Boys and girls, men and women alike receive these messages. Valuing us *most* for our bodies is an attitude which has been around for so long that it can feel normal for both men and women. And questioning the norm can feel risky or uncomfortable, even threatening.

As well, the dominant culture places high value on products, production, productivity and reproduction. And it tends to link Womanhood with the ability to bear children, often viewing those of us who don't have children as somehow having failed as women. A case in point is that it is common for many of us to feel we have proved our value as women when we become pregnant. The potential to reproduce has been so thoroughly linked to Womanhood that labels like "barren" and "childless" have been used to negate any further identity for a woman.[30] These are not neutral terms. In contrast, "barren" and "childless" are rarely used to describe men. While individual men certainly feel their masculinity threatened by infertility, society still values men far more for their skills and for what they accomplish than for their bodies or reproductive capacity. In a far more profound way than with a man, those of us without children risk being considered— and considering ourselves—as less than complete.

Despite changes in women's roles during the last few decades, the majority culture still teaches females and males that proof of ultimate *womanhood* rests in a combination of motherhood and partnership with a male. While many women and men *know* that there is a great deal more to being a woman, this knowledge is not transmitted to all members of our society with the same force and consistency as the former message.

When a culture considers the ability to bear children to be our *most important function as women,* fertility becomes synonymous with Essence of Womanhood. Then the fertile years become the *most* valued years and the nonfertile years less valued. Contrast, for example, that in some cultures aging women—that is, women who are no longer fertile—move to a *different, yet equal* value for their perspectives, wisdom and experience. Despite the many changes women in the majority culture have experienced in the last 30 years or so, our *most prominent* value remains centered on the sexual and reproductive capacities of our bodies.

This is as opposed to what we *do*. And thus, *Essence of Womanhood, attractiveness and sexual desirability are thoroughly linked to the body and appearance—and only during the fertile years*. And, for most of us, those fertile years end with menopause. I believe that, as women, we intuitively know that we naturally have a great deal to offer society in addition to our sexual and reproductive capacities. Because this fact is not openly acknowledged and discussed, it makes sense that some of us can feel sad, confused and angry during menopause.

There is no disputing that the capacity to bear children that most of us have is wondrous, valuable and essential to our species and a deeply significant experience in many of our lives. However, unless *comparable value* is placed in other realms, fertility becomes firmly intertwined with what it means to be feminine, sexually desirable and valued *as a woman*. The enormity of the impact of this equation on those of us in and beyond menopause—and on men and children—can be difficult to fully comprehend. The confusion, sorrow and anger brought about by this situation was central to the women's experiences of menopause.

9
I Felt As Though I Was Losing My Femininity

Because menopause—like menstruation—is unique to women, it is, by definition, feminine. It would seem reasonable to expect that women and men would find both menstruation and menopause to be the most feminine of experiences. Instead, the reverse is most often the case.

To varying degrees the women felt that with menopause they were losing some of what they called "femininity." At the same time there was a nagging concern that this meant they were vain or somehow not modern, liberated women. They tended to feel this most strongly in the early years of menopause.

"In a nutshell, I feel unfeminine; not attractive to men."

"I felt very sexless. . . . I worried that I might become this strange amorphous creature. I almost felt like I had become a man. I mean, I was afraid that I had lost all my feminine hormones and that I didn't look feminine any more. . . . I started feeling like I wasn't really a woman."

"I felt like I'd lost my attractiveness."

"Menopause changed the man-woman dynamic for me because *post*menopausally, I feel like I'm not as able to *compete* in some of the stereotypical ways that I was able to premenopausally. I put on weight. And slimmer women are more attractive. I have hot flashes, which I found *the* most unattractive part of it all. And I also wasn't calm and gracious and flirtatious. I wasn't as *capable* of that mode of behavior."

"My husband thinks I should go on hormone therapy because my sex drive is so low these days. I'm not sure *why* I don't feel as sexy as I used to, but I'm not sure taking hormones will fix it. It feels deeper. It feels more complicated than that. I think it has to do with how I'm feeling about myself."

"I don't think Jim finds me any less attractive, sexually, these days. It's *me* who feels less desirable. I used to revel in my womanliness. I *enjoyed* being a woman. Now I feel like I've lost it. And I don't know where it went. All I know is that I want it back! And it's so frustrating because I don't think I could explain any of this to Jim in a million years. I don't even know what to tell him I need from him. I think if I could, he'd do it. What a mess!"

What is this "femininity" these women are speaking of? It is a set of cultural standards and expectations about how women should appear and behave. In general, cultures tend to strictly define acceptable male and female looks and actions. These standards vary from culture to culture, and within a culture from one historical period to another. Much of what our North American media portrays as feminine, attractive and desirable may be seen as unattractive in other cultures. An example is attitudes toward slimness: in some countries too little meat on the bones looks and feels too much like starvation to be seen as desirable. Even within Western civilization, what we popularly think of as beautiful or feminine has changed over time. For example, the weight and shape of Venus as portrayed by various artists over the centuries as a symbol of beauty, has varied greatly. By today's standards she has been overweight for much of her existence.

For some of the lesbians I have spoken with, issues of conventioanl attractiveness and desirability in the face of aging had little relevance to them. For others, it did. It is no more appropriate to generalize to all lesbian's experiences than it is to all heterosexual women's experiences. A thorough exploration of the lesbian experience of menopause is a story waiting to be told. And when it is, it will serve to inform the experiences of all women, regardless of sexual orientation.

Susan Brownmiller, in her book, *Femininity*, writes that in the majority culture, the domain of femininity includes appropriate dress, movement, skin, voice, manner, and body size, shape and age. A woman who is young, slim and shapely, with unwrinkled and unblemished skin is the essence of currently-defined femininity. She dresses demurely or sexily, and restricts her movement (by high heels, tight skirts, coiffed hair, make up and snagable nylons). Her voice is soft and modulated. Her manner is characterized by a certain self-consciousness, vulnerability and passivity. She has a caring nature and values both mother and romantic love.[32]

Contrast this image with those of us whose age, body shape and skin reflect a wealth of experience and emotion, and perhaps a life of hard work and pregnancies; a woman who may have placed more emphasis on what she did rather than on maintaining a youthful shape. Her dress and shoes allow unrestricted movement. Her voice is comfortable with a full range of expression, including authority and anger. Her manner reflects strength and self assurance and, perhaps, a current lack of interest in either mother or romantic love. While this description may be appealing or include many of us, it does not reflect what is popularly considered to be "feminine."

Brownmiller points out that most of us experience a lot of pressure from society to keep this femininity. Strong, independent women have found themselves softening and toning down their voices, manner and opinions so as to keep a feminine aura. It requires a good deal of energy and money to maintain this femininity. It is interesting to contemplate what we could do with this energy and money if these standards of attractiveness were closer to who we are, *as is*.

For many of us, the characteristics of what the majority culture calls feminine are still a route to social status and power. As Robin Lakoff and Raquel Scherr note, the traditional ideal that we should be beautiful, desirable and attract men is alive and well today.[33]

"I hate to admit it, but brains aside, that's what I want, because that's what men—and other women— value the most."

"No matter how successful I am in other areas, there's still a part of me that feels I've failed. Because it feels like in the eyes of the world I've never quite measured up. I'm not beautiful or refined or quiet."

Because this ideal has a lot of power, many of us either secretly long to be this ideal or are angry at those who achieve it.

A study which looked at what is considered to be attractive in males and females found that when subjects rated photos of the same people at youth, middle age, and old age, aging women were thought to diminish in attractiveness to a greater extent than aging men. Ratings of men's masculinity remained fairly constant over the lifespan, whereas women's perceived femininity declined rapidly with aging.[34] Feminine beauty standards stress youthfulness far more heavily than masculine standards.

Over the years of menopause the door to our youth gradually closes. At the same time in our North American dominant culture, popular notions of femininity, sexual desirability and attractiveness are based on youth. Is it any wonder so many of us report anxiety, sadness or depression at menopause? This is an untenable situation.

Desire and Desirability

Ask yourself how old a woman has to be before most of us think she is distasteful for dressing or acting sensuously. The answer is strictly cultural. Vivian Gornick, in her book *In Search of Ali Mahmoud* reports on a perspective from another culture:

"What was great....was the sexiness of the women, the older women acting as sexy and drunkenly self-assured as the younger woman. Women of fifty behaving as though they considered themselves as desirable as their twenty-five-year-old daughters. And, indeed, they were, the men caressing and courting them as often as they did the younger women; and the older women responding or ignoring, accepting or repelling, with the same degree of lustful vanity that their daughters displayed. If I had gone up to one of these be-wigged Melina Mercouris and said to her, 'Listen, where I come from. . . .any woman [your age] who. . . .acts as you're doing now does so out of nervous desperation, and everyone feels contempt and pity, like she doesn't know her *place*,' she would surely have. . . .replied, 'But I do not understand. I am alive, no? And while I desire I am desirable, no?'"[35]

Unlike many other cultures, those of us who are older women in our North American majority culture may ask ourselves how appropriate it is to act on our sensual feelings. Not surprisingly, many of us come to *believe* we are no longer attractive or desirable after menopause. And this can leave us vulnerable to taking on responsibility for any lack of ability or interest our lovers may experience. With respect to male lovers, it may be helpful to remember that it is the male, not the female, who is usually less able to act on his sexual interest as he ages.[36] We need to keep in mind that menopause is an unfolding, a progression in our sexual life, not an ending. In fact, we may find that the end of the period of fertility may *increase* our sexual capabilities.

As "older women," our sexual desire is also influenced by our opportunities for sex with *interested* and *interesting* partners.[37] Rita Freedman points out that, for heterosexual women, the biggest sexual problem is not lack of interest or responsiveness but lack of a partner:

"While this is partially the product of greater female longevity, it is also caused by the decision of many men to marry younger women and by the double standard that brands older women as unattractive and therefore sexually undesirable."[38]

Nelson Aldrich, Jr., in a fascinating article in the January, 1992, issue of *Lear's* magazine, comments on the differences he sees between European and North American women. Although he uses the term "European" somewhat loosely, he makes some interesting points. For example, he questions why European culture seems to not only give women the means to be beautiful, but men and boys the eyes to see that beauty. He suggests that we, as North American women, have learned that there comes a time when our youth, and with it our beauty and desirability, must be passed on to the younger generation "as a precious jewel might be passed on, for the daughter to have, and the mother, alas, to have no longer."[39] Whereas, he notes:

"In Europe, no self-respecting mother would dream of surrendering her beauty and desirability to anyone, least of all to her daughter. . . . Maturity often brings with it in Europe a flourishing force of character and a wisdom of the flesh that together yield a terrific erotic power, to be played out on husbands or lovers according to personal taste, moral virtue, and social opportunity. The consolation, if any is needed, comes from the mother's knowledge that it is she who is envied by her daughter, not the other way around."[40]

The Pressure to Stay in "Control" to Keep "Femininity"

According to the popular ideal, a "feminine" woman controls or contains her emotions, body size, shape and reproductive system. And this particular control is potentially threatened, or at least in question, during menopause. Not surprisingly, one of the most common feelings reported by the women I worked with was that of feeling out of control.

In our majority culture, a "feminine" woman controls her anger—a most *un*feminine emotion. Therefore, a woman with her mouth set tightly, brow furrowed, eyes narrowed in anger, is not feminine. In contrast, a man with a similar expression loses none of his masculinity; in fact, he may even enhance it. Recall the number of movies in which the hero is a man angry at the status quo. And note how few movies have a woman in a similar role. Conversely, the popular image of masculinity can be threatened when a man shows sadness or fear; whereas, these same emotions are seen to heighten the image of femininity in the eyes of the dominant culture.

For many of us, it is far more acceptable and often safer to cry than to show anger. For others of us, anger may show up as depression or physical illness. As Susan Brownmiller notes, "the price of inhibited anger and a nonviolent temperament may well be a bucketful of tears."[41] When irritation (a less problematic emotion) turns to anger, the possibility of our being labelled "hysterical" or "out of control" is considerably higher. This is part of the image of the stereotypical "menopausal woman."

The struggle to reach the popular ideal of femininity/attractiveness requires that we try to control our body size and shape. However, sometimes we can't attribute weight gained during menopause to "lack of restraint"; that is, to eating "too much" or exercising "too little". Those extra pounds may then cause us to feel that we have, in some way, lost control over our body. These changes are often unexpected and can leave many of us feeling we have been betrayed by our body: after all, we didn't *do* anything out of line. Although we may have followed the "rules," our body changed. Robin Lakoff and Raquel Scherr note that today's intense focus on weight has moved out of the realm of health and activity. Instead, it has become yet another area in which many of us feel inadequate, depressed or out of control.[42] Ironically and unfortunately, some women may be unaware that a gain of five to ten pounds may serve as a hedge against osteoporosis.[43]

Body changes we can't control can include the appearance of coarser facial hair. Some of us get a few beard-like hairs on our chin during menopause. These hairs usually remain few in number, lessening or disappearing after menopause.[44] At the time, however, they can feel to us like visible proof that feminine hormones are slipping away: further evidence that our body is "out of control." The smooth, hairless skin of childhood is a requirement of beauty in North American women. While the more rebellious of us may forego shaving our legs and underarms, few of us permit a visible display of hair on our chin or chest. In contrast, European women often express astonishment over North American attitudes about body hair on women.

Hot flashes and night sweats, which can also feel uncontrollable, are not included in mainstream ideas of the "feminine" woman. During a hot flash we may feel that our aging process (*and all that that means*) is visible for the world to see: that is, we are not controlling it. And we may feel less desirable as a sexual partner while having night sweats. With sweat-soaked sheets and body we may be more likely to prefer being alone. Given that the mind is the most powerful sex organ we have, it would not be surprising if sex were far from our minds at the time. It is not the hot flash itself that is the problem. Rather it is the completely unrealistic, unattainable ideal of the so-called feminine woman— and that many of us feel, while in menopause, that we are further than we've ever been from this ideal.

The fitness craze aside, the popular view says that sweat is anything *but* feminine, and sweat stains advertise it for the world to see. Susan Brownmiller writes:

> "Rivulets of dampness that soak the shirt and mat the hair are honorable emblems in a man of action who earns his bread by the sweat of his brow. . . . But there is no situation in which perspiration enhances the feminine aura. . . . Sweat on the brow defeats the attempt to look untouched and untroubled. Beaded moisture on the lip does not give the impression of sweet, quiet grace. A patch of wetness spreading under the arms is incompatible with genteel refinement, with fresh spring-flower loveliness that is calm, cool and collected."[45]

The process of trying to meet the popular ideal of femininity requires that we try to control *where* moisture appears on our body: not on brow, above the lip, under the arms or otherwise running down our bodies. However, moist lips and vagina are desirable.

Most of the women noticed some change in the degree of moisture in their vaginas during menopause.[46]

Although this was not necessarily a serious problem in their sex lives, they often felt less desirable as a result: "I didn't feel very receptive. My vagina felt *inhospitable*, like an inhospitable environment." A drier vagina became a sign of getting old, or of "not being able to cut it any more."

Misunderstandings about a drier vagina can complicate love-making in ways often difficult to discuss directly. A moist vagina traditionally signals that we are ready and available for sex. Therefore, some of the women felt silently accused by their lovers of not being aroused, which was not always the case. In turn, as one woman put it, this brought on feelings of "confusion and fear and sorrow—and then some anger."

"To him it meant that *he* was not capable of arousing me to the point where I was producing juice, that it was a reflection on him. So he didn't like the thought of me using KY jelly."

"Even with hormones, I'm still drier in the vagina. I find using cremes really embarrassing and a real turn-off. And I take it personally. I feel lacking....I don't feel as feminine, that way."

On the other hand, given the threats to attractiveness which come with menopause in the majority culture, it would not be surprising if we require more foreplay and reassurance of our desirability before we feel aroused. It seems reasonable to consider that, as menopausal women, our feelings about ourselves *as a woman* might, to some degree at least, influence our vaginal moisture.

Trying to control our body's moisture can be a

consistent chore in many of our lives. As women, we walk a fine line between wet, but not too wet. Our faces "shouldn't" appear shiny, suggesting sweat or oilyness, while dryness, promoting wrinkles, is the enemy. Again, wrinkles make visible what our majority culture tells us to keep hidden: the fact that we are aging. A common message in the media today is: "You are now okay as an older woman, as long as you *look* like a younger woman." This places enormous pressure on many of us to stop the natural process of aging, to struggle even harder to achieve a feminine ideal which is based on a youthful body.

As Susan Sontag notes:

"In a man's face lines are taken to be signs of 'character.' They indicate emotional strength, maturity—qualities far more esteemed in men than in women. (They show he has 'lived.')....But lines of aging [in women] ....are regarded as unfortunate blemishes....A woman's face is prized so far as it remains unchanged by (or conceals the traces of) her emotions, her physical risk-taking. Ideally, it is supposed to be a mask— immutable, unmarked."[47]

Advertisers step in to try to convince us that we *can* control the aging process. The language used to describe wrinkles and aging in women refers to either withering fruit or a battle to combat a degenerating system. Phrases such as "winning the wrinkle wars," and "subduing the enemy"[48] are common in advertising. A recent popular magazine article on controlling wrinkles reflects the importance placed on controlling our emotions in order to remain "feminine." Referring to "expression lines," the author notes, "dermatologists have had some success teaching people to control their facial muscles."[49] Use of the word, "people" softens what this statement is saying: *women,* not *people,* are the ones being given the message that we need to control our emotions so as not to "lose the wrinkle war."

Consider the following advertisement in a popular women's magazine: "Wrinkles are the result of *structural damage.* The skin's *support has crumbled* and the only way to *repair* it is to *rebuild* that structure [italics mine]."[50] Again, this is a cultural view of our body as a *factory*—a description of a system out of control, damaged and failing. Such images can promote panic in many of us and can guarantee that we will separate ourselves from our bodies in an attempt to survive the "war." With such disturbing images, it is no wonder so many of us in the majority culture feel compelled to *combat* the aging process, and often believe that taking extra hormones is the way to do this.

When we are able, instead, to think of our aging as change and development rather than as degeneration, then our faces with our lines of smiles and worries clearly show the world our character and strength as women of deep emotion. Then we can see that our faces honor both our experiences and our natural progression through life.

"Will My Partner's Feelings About Me Change?"

If we feel we have lost some attractiveness, we may understandably wonder if our partner still holds the same feelings toward us. After all, the value and attractiveness of older women is not generally recognized. Nor is it talked about. Nor is it sung, painted, danced or written about in the same way it is of younger women. During menopause some of us can feel this absence as a *confirmation* of loss of value. How differently would we think of menopause if images of older women as robust, sensual and beautiful beings were as common as the images of youthful attractiveness which currently surround us?

Jean Baker Miller in her book, *Toward a New Psychology of Women*, discusses the significance of connection in the lives of women (and, by association, in the lives of men and children). She notes that, as women, most of us stay with, build on, and develop in a context of connections with others. Indeed, our sense of self becomes very much organized around being able to make and then to maintain relationships.[51]

In general, as women, we are rooted in a sense of connection. Miller points out that most of us learn very young that connection is central to our lives. She adds that our mainstream culture has not cherished, or even recognized, this characteristic and strength in women. On the contrary, many of us have found that if we act on the basis of this underlying psychological motive, we risk being thought of, and seeing ourselves, as suffering from emotional problems.[52] Too often a woman's efforts to maintain connections are misunderstood. Too often they are seen as signs of "being needy."

Carol Gilligan, in her ground-breaking book, *In A Different Voice: Psychological Theory and Women's Development*, explains how she sees the difference between men and women in their needs for connection:

"Relationships, and particularly issues of dependency, are experienced differently by women and men. For boys and men, separation and individuation are critically tied to gender identity since separation from the mother is essential for the development of masculinity. For girls and women, issues of femininity or feminine identity do not depend on the achievement of separation from the mother or on the progress of individuation. Since masculinity is defined through separation while femininity is defined through attachment, male gender identity is threatened by intimacy while female gender identity is threatened by separation."[53]

For many of us, sex can serve as a powerful expression of connection with our partners. Our unity with our partner may feel threatened if we have begun to doubt our sexual attractiveness. Then, an anxiety difficult to name may invade our bedroom, complicating the relationship and heightening insecurities on both sides. In the majority culture, our sexual attractiveness *does* come into question during and following menopause. Although this is absurd, the fact remains that menopause signals a movement away from the traits which most men—and most women—find appealing. However, the lesbian women I have spoken to report feeling more protected from cultural messages about what constitutes female attractiveness. But regardless of sexual orientation, women in strong relationships will no doubt be more protected. They are more likely to have open and honest lines of communication about sex, as well as understanding partners who value them *far beyond* sexuality or youth. For those not in strong relationships, menopause may feel like a threat to an already-shakey connection with their partners.

* * * * * * * * * *

Many of us believe only we—and perhaps a handful

of other "lesser women"—are insecure about our aging or femininity. We often see other women as not having the same problems, as being more attractive, more interesting, or as so strong or so intelligent that they are not affected in the way we are. But, in fact, it is only the rare woman in the majority culture who can remain completely unaffected by its standards of attractiveness and value.

It is both natural and protective to hide what we feel is considered unacceptable. Cosmetics, stylish clothes and the right hairdo provide many of us with a measure of cover and protection. In a culture which values us primarily for functions associated with our bodies, this is more about *security* than vanity. Make-up and clothes are not the issue, the impossibility of the feminine ideal is.

Virtually every aspect of what is popularly considered to be "feminine" is challenged during menopause. This would not be so serious if something of *equal cultural value* replaced it—such as, for example, recognition for accumulated female wisdom. I have been told that this recognition is more readily given among lesbians and may explain the protection they feel from dominant cultural messages. If we can understand menopause as a part of our emotional and physical development, we can go a long way toward correcting this imbalance in the dominant culture. Then *we*, personally, are more likely to accept that our attractiveness and sensuality do not lessen or end with menopause. Rather, we can recognize that we go through interesting and desirable changes.

As woman we account for just over half of the population of this planet and most of us raise this planet's children. That is a lot of power. Although this power has tended to be historically unacknowledged and devalued by both sexes, we are potentially a major force in our society because we are the majority. I believe that if we openly share our experiences of menopause and aging with each other, we can use this knowledge and power to create new ideas of femininity and attractiveness and begin to change the attitudes and values which are damaging to women and, by extension, to children and men.

PART 2

To everything there is a season....
A time to plant and a time to pluck what is planted....
A time to break down and a time to build up,
A time to weep and a time to dance
A time to cast away stones and a time to gather stones....
A time to gain and a time to lose....
A time to keep silence and a time to speak....

– Ecclesiastes 3:1

Adolescence is the flip side of menopause, and we think

of it as part of a person's development. Why, then, do

we not think of menopause in the same way?

10
Menopause= Development, Not Decline

Once through menopause many of the women felt they had reconnected with a part of themselves which they had left behind many years ago in early adolescence. They also came to see that their menopause, like their adolescence, had played a significant role in their on-going psychological and physical development as female persons. Both were times of hormonal changes which were naturally accompanied by subtle—and not so subtle—changes in their sense of self as females.

Emerging

"There was a real impression of changing and emerging, and of not being sure of what or who I was....It felt like I was starting to come out of something, and I was not sure I wanted to, or of what I was going to be....Menopause brought a change that was forced. It wasn't one that I chose; but it was an inevitable process."

"Once I knew I had completed menopause for sure, I felt *released*. Something got freed up in me."

"I'm getting more and more energy. . . .When all is said and done, I feel like a heroine, that I survived, and my marriage survived!"

"I feel joy. I never had children, and now the whole question is no longer an issue, so I feel more expansive about the future."

"With menopause it felt as though I'd come to a sharp curve in a path that was unexpected—in terms of something that would change me. I had no idea of what was around that corner, except that I'd be different, and I didn't know how. Now that I'm around that corner, I feel like I'm in a whole new territory."

"I've finished with something that's been winding down for a long time now. I haven't sorted out what all that means to me. I'd sure love to read about this ending-beginning place I'm at right now."

On the surface, menopause seemed to be a fairly insignificant event in the lives of most of the women. However, after the women had told their stories and uncovered what menopause meant to them, a different picture emerged. As it turned out, menopause had more of an influence on them than they had originally thought: it had been an undercurrent affecting many of their feelings and behaviors over the months and years of menopause.

Menopause was clearly a transition in the women's lives. And the changes they experienced suggest that a process of personal development was occurring. This implied a new way of thinking and talking about menopause.

Unexplored Territory

Not so long ago, it was generally thought that the only serious psychological and physical development in either sex occurred from birth to about 18-21 years. Development was what happened to us *up to* adulthood, not *during* adulthood. Today, developmental researchers recognize that we continue to grow and change throughout our lives. Still, the study of adult development remains in its infancy compared with the relatively advanced state of knowledge we have about childhood and adolescence. For example, we now differentiate between infancy and toddlerhood, the preschool child, middle childhood and early, middle and late adolescence. The knowledge we have acquired about these phases allows us a broader awareness of the needs of persons from birth to the end of adolescence. Because of this knowledge, we are more able to understand each of these stages even though there is still much to learn about the period from birth through adolescence.

Although research on adult life has been on the increase in the past decade, "much of the life span—especially the years from twenty to sixty-five—remains in large part unexplored."[54] Perhaps most significantly, we have little idea of what the *interaction* of the changing emotional, physical and spiritual needs of those over 20 might be. As Joanne Stevenson observes:

"As children, North Americans are taught to believe that being grown-up is one long static plateau that lasts until old age, and this belief is reinforced regularly. Such early assumptions have not been dispelled in the educational processes to date, so people carry false assumptions about adulthood into their middle years."[55]

Women Are Not Men

Our traditional ways of thinking about adult development are not without serious problems. Like most theories, they have cultural biases because researchers, like the rest of us, are subject to the attitudes and "truths" of their culture. While this does not necessarily make entire theories invalid, it is important to understand that all philosophies, theories and research sit on a foundation of cultural beliefs and values.

Like our theories of "good health," our traditional theories of psychological development have been based on the study of males, and have rarely included the study of females. Instead, human development has been equated with male development. These developmental theories have established men's experience and competence as a baseline from which women are compared. As a result, women are too often judged as abnormal for not adhering to the male pattern. In general, we think, write and speak about development and levels of maturity have not incorporated the female experience. Rather, they are based on the study of one sex only. From this position, our society has considered and judged both men's and women's development.[56]

These theories explain the female lifespan by using men as the norm—and are based on the ways in which we, as females, conform to, or diverge from, patterns found in the study of males. Consequently, as Jessie Bernard notes in *Women, Wives and Mothers*, when developmental theorists do discuss women lives, they do so in terms of our reproductive cycle or equate women's development with the family life cycle. Our major theories of adult development do not include the possibility that, as women, we may view our world differently than men, and, because of that different view, may have some different values.

Some researchers and practitioners are now taking a closer look at the lives of girls and women.[57] They note that in our society males and females learn very different ways of being in the world. *And, when women are used as the frame of reference, a very different picture emerges of what is "normal" for women.* One area being re-examined with women's lives as the focus is the way in which we have traditionally viewed self-development, emotional growth and maturity. In the past, achieving maturity has been assumed to require separating oneself from others and becoming "one's own man." Theories based on males suggest that, for males, this is a desirable and empowering process, a goal to strive for. In contrast, research indicates that for females, *relationships* play a more central role in our personal development. As girls and women, most of us tend to emphasize the power and importance of our *connections with*—rather than our separation from—others.

First, this research into female development suggests that we need to re-examine what we mean by maturity and how we achieve it. The definition which focuses on becoming psychologically independent of others and "gaining" individual achievement is too narrow. Clearly, maturity is also about taking the responsibility for making meaningful connections with others, and having the ability to do so. As women, most of us find that our sense of self occurs *within* emotional connections with others, not separate from them.[58] And not only are the traditional ways of thinking about growth of self and maturity inappropriate for women—they may also be less than adequate for men. As Jean Baker Miller notes, "few men ever attain such self-sufficiency, as every woman knows."[59]

Secondly, when we evaluate traditional theories in the light of women's experiences it becomes necessary to re-examine our standards of both mental and physical health. With women as the norm, what does maturity, aging, emotional expression or a healthy body look like? What appears neurotic, needy, problematic or hysterical from one perspective may be interestingly varied—and normal—behavior from another.

Today, mental health continues to be defined by what is seen to be healthy for males. As Carol Gilligan notes, "in the life cycle, as in the Garden of Eden, the woman has been the deviant."[60] Traditionally, the psychology of females has been defined in male terms. And it has been discussed as if it were created solely by biology, *as seen from a male perspective.* This view suggests that we are best understood in relation to the physical workings of our bodies. While this can be a problem for many of us throughout our lives, it is especially so during menopause. It keeps the other sides of menopause hidden: *what menopause means to us and how that affects us physically.*

A third point about traditional developmental theories and research is that they tend to consider the changes of adulthood—including menopause—in terms of decline. *This is an outcome of seeing the human body and mind as a factory with an emphasis on production—and a definition of efficiency which is based on that view.* Therefore, we have a focus on deteriorating functions, rather than including those which may increase, or change in their nature. Instead of simply deterioration, the idea of *change* is equally valid—and change can be about growth or decline, or some third combination of the two. In the majority culture there is little common wisdom about areas of improvement or increased maturity with aging.[61] If there were, it is not hard to imagine that societal views of menopause would change.

Cultures which are not youth-focused—such as many Native American, Asian and some European cultures—more often recognize the increased wisdom, perspective, communication and healing powers of their elders. As Judith Stevens-Long notes in *Adult Life: Developmental Processes:*

> "American scientists almost always assume that a person's performance can only increase, decrease, or remain stable. They have rarely considered the possibility that some processes are exceedingly complex and must be treated as an array of functions, some declining with age, some remaining stable or improving, and some even undergoing transformation with the years."[62]

We're living longer these days. Consequently, we may have to broaden our perspectives on development in both sexes if we are to truly grow old gracefully.[63]

About Transitions

Life, mirroring nature, is about changes. Transitions are times when we adjust to change and integrate that change. They are about movement from one place, situation, or way of viewing ourselves or the world, to another. And they play a role in our ongoing, life-long psychological development. Because transitions provide us with new perspectives on ourselves, others, and the world around us, they spur some of our most significant emotional and intellectual growth.

Our lifespan is made up of many transitions, some large, some small, some visible, some not. They are usually woven into the fabric of our lives as we carry on with daily living.

As often as not, we don't know we're in a transition until we are through it and able to look back. Only then, if we reflect on it, can we see its significance in our lives.

Some transitions, such as moving from one apartment to another, may be over within a short time. Others, such as moving to a different town and developing a new social circle, take longer. Still others, like adolescence and menopause, are "life transitions" that span a number of years.

Some may be visible and easily identified by others; for example, the appearance of a baby which marks the transition into motherhood or fatherhood. Others may be less visible—as the death of a last parent marks a transition to oldest-generation status.

Several small or large transitions in various areas of our lives may overlap at any one time, along with periods of relative stability in other areas. Adjusting to the last child leaving home may co-exist with a stable and comfortable job. Life is not a clearly defined progression from periods of complete stability, through change, to stability again. Rather, many things go on at the same time.

Keeping these characteristics of development and transition in mind gives us an interesting view of the women's experiences of menopause.

"The Change" Versus "Menopause"

The women with whom I've worked clearly saw menopause as a transition bringing change. This is demonstrated, in part, by their response to the word "menopause."

"I've always thought of change as a long process, and that's where 'menopause' doesn't do it....It sounds like a simple door you walk through, and instead of that, there's this long, convoluted process that involves all sorts of aspects."

"My mother always referred to it as a 'change of life.' I don't think I ever heard her use the word 'menopause.'"

"What I'm trying to say is that 'menopause' doesn't *fit*, it doesn't *work*. I'm craving for some other, I don't know, *word*.

"With a change I get the idea of time through it. Change in a person doesn't usually happen overnight. The way the medicals define menopause, I don't get a feeling of change. Change is what I went through. And that was unexpected for me. It kind of caught me unawares."

"I never heard the word 'menopause' until I was old enough to know a bit of biology. It's like using the word 'voiding' or something. My physician asked me if I'd *voided*. Pardon me!....I *hate* the word 'menopause'! Nobody would use it in a poem.... whereas when I think of 'The Change' or 'change of life' I think of older women sitting around drinking tea or sherry, and having a whale of a time."

"I think 'menopause' and I cringe. It gives me a bad taste in my mouth. I mean, I really don't feel I'm having a hard time aging. I *admire* the old women in my family and don't mind becoming just like them;

but there's just something about that word that makes my skin crawl! I can actually *feel* myself pulling away from any association with it."

What the word "menopause" meant to these women did not reflect what their experience meant to them. As a *description* of their changes, "menopause" got a failing grade: it often suggested illness, disease and negativity. The women thought of it as a term *owned* by the medical profession, rather than by them. As one of the women said so passionately:

"I have a hard time connecting the word 'menopause' with a celebration of *living* and *growing* and *changing*— which is what I'm doing."

The women wanted words that painted a picture of a natural progression through life. They wanted to convey a feeling of personally owning or belonging to the process. For them, "The Change" or "the change of life," had this potential. Most significantly, these expressions came closer to describing what they went through. And these words have the added advantage of having a historical connection with their mothers and grandmothers—a connection to a universal female experience.

11
After Menopause: Looking Back

"**I**'m glad it's over. It's not that I had a bad time of it or anything. It's just that now I feel more secure or something."

"I've got myself back again. I really like me now (laughing)!"

"It's been years since I've felt this calm in myself."

"I feel different, stronger than I was."

"Even though I didn't notice menopause all that much, I feel a lot lighter now. I don't know why that is. More comfortable in my own skin these days."

For the most part, the women I've worked with emerged from menopause feeling on firmer, more secure ground. For one, they were no longer concerned about pregnancy or its responsibilities. And they were free of the inconvenience and the potential for embarrassment which, in the majority culture, often goes along with menstruating.

Other changes were more difficult to articulate. Again, they made sense of their experiences by discussing them with each other.

"I've been thinking about what's different in me, now that I'm through menopause. Sure, six years have passed and there's been some changes in my life that have nothing to do with menopause, but what I'm talking about has to do with me as a woman. There's a difference and I can feel it."

"For a long time when I was in menopause I felt like I'd lost a lot of my femininity, my femaleness. Now that a couple more years have gone by I don't feel that any more. I don't mean I've got it back in the same way I had before, but it is different now."

"It's almost embarrassing to say, but part of me feels more like a kid now than I have since I *was* a kid. My body is definitely matronly and not young so I feel as though I'm supposed to be acting mature or something. I don't know. I feel a little foolish saying it—sounds like I'm *regressing* or something! (laughing) Perish the thought! But when I hit adolescence I changed. Something about me got set aside then. That's the part I'm feeling again now. Feels great! I think that as a young girl I had some interesting things going for me. Now, I'm kind of catching up with them again."

"These days, I'm not as, I don't know, *afraid* to just

be me. Don't get me wrong, I certainly haven't been walking around in fear all these years! I consider myself a fairly tough person. Still, (pause) that's it. It doesn't feel as though there are as many *barriers* to me being just me. I think it's exciting. Every now and then I catch my guy and my son looking at me as if to say, 'Who *is* this person?' I wonder what they'd say if someone asked them how I've changed? Or if they'd even be able to say. I think I'll ask them anyway. The answer might be interesting!"

"I really didn't know who I was during menopause! Now I feel more connected with who I really am, more settled in myself."

"Being *post*-menopausal brought me back to who I was before all the stuff connected to reproduction and nurturing and having to watch myself. Now that I'm past menopause I feel very different about clothes and make up and pleasing a man. Somehow I feel freed up from all that. It's just not as important anymore. I don't mean that I don't care about how I *look* or creating a great meal for my family. I do. But my *motivation* is different. Do you know what I mean? Like, makeup and hairdos are more for fun now. The difference is, I don't feel as though I *have* to as much. And way deep down, I used to. I'm stronger in myself now."

"When I was around 12, before I started my periods, I felt like a very *powerful* person. I wasn't a woman. And I wasn't ever going to be, as far as I could figure out. It just seemed like I didn't have a lot of the encumbrances that I've had since, as a woman. Then

I felt free to be *anything*. Today I feel like that again.
I can believe that again."

"It's like I, *me* is more able to come out now. For
an awful long time a part of me has been tucked
away somewhere. There wasn't really *room* for it in
my life before."

These are powerful statements about significant
changes, about a certain liberation and feelings of greater
inner strength and power. A shift had occurred in how
the women saw themselves as women—a shift
precipitated by the meanings they associated with the
physical changes of menopause.

The women often referred to parts of themselves in
girlhood as "the real me." In various ways they spoke
of feeling freed up to re-connect with parts of themselves
which had been developing *prior to their first menstrual
period*. In the years between their first period and the
onset of menopause, they had of course, grown, evolved
and matured: they were women with rich histories of
growth and development. However, their experiences
suggest that the changes they under went during
menopause created a time of *accelerated* development
so that, after menopause, they had more access to long-
submerged portions of themselves. They felt *more able*
to experience and nurture these parts of themselves.

For those of us in the majority culture, beginning
to menstruate usually meant we were beginning the
process of becoming a woman. Most of us then
experienced certain subtle social pressures to meet the
standards of "femininity." As Emily Hancock notes in
The Girl Within, "in donning the masks provided by
the culture, a girl easily loses sight of who and what

she is beneath the feminine facade she adopts in youth."[64] As women who no longer menstruate, many of us experience some release from the pressures of "femininity." Once past menopause, many of us are more able, or have more opportunity, to reveal who we are under the mask of culturally defined femininity. However, the extent to which we can act on this freedom depends on individual, social and economic factors.

Subtle Changes in Sense of Self-as-Woman

Male or female, who we are as a person is not separate from our gender: our male or femaleness is naturally very much a part of how we see ourselves and how others see us. Given what is valued in femaleness in the majority culture, and given the extent to which this value is threatened during menopause, the physical changes of menopause cannot help but influence our sense of female identity. The experiences of the women I have worked with suggest that women in menopause may be adjusting to a new female identity—one which has nothing to do with fertility and its many subtle associations and meanings.

"I remember I went through years wondering whether I was going to come out as a butterfly or a moth. But, the creature that comes out doesn't fit anywhere. I mean, what is a woman? Someone who bears children? Someone who is attractive to men? Someone who cares for people? And, the woman who comes out of menopause doesn't necessarily *want* to be any of those things. I mean, she may still want to be attractive, but perhaps by society's standards she isn't anymore. She *can't* have children *and* she may no longer have this great wish to care for everybody.

So, who is she/me?. . .It's not that it's not exciting,
but it's scary too, because there's no anchor."

A former role, identity or part of the women's sense
of self-as-woman—and the value attached to it—had
come to an end with menopause. Consciously or
unconsciously they had to adjust to who they were
outside that former identity-as-woman. It seems natural
that they would return to who they were becoming
before their first menstruation, before the time when
most of them felt pressure to take on the constraints
of majority culture "femininity."

This experience is echoed by Jane Ussher, in her book,
The Psychology of the Female Body. She notes that for
most menopausal women, along with completing
menstruation and no longer being defined through
reproduction, there is a cessation of other aspects of
our identity—those which are bound up with being
fertile, capable of mothering and of being a young
woman.[65]

"I'd lost the ability to be a mother for all time. This
had an incredible effect on me."

"Every once in a while I find myself thinking that,
oh, but I can't have another child. And, I mean, it
really *surprises* me, even though it's four years since
I've even *had* a period and 14 years since I had the
tubal ligation!"

"When I went to the doctor and she said that I was
*post*menopausal, I realized immediately that means
I can't have any more children. And I don't want
any more children. That didn't matter. It was: I *can't*

have any more children. It was like a *weight* on my chest. I know it's *true*, but I don't really believe it."

"Having children is a deep human experience. The issue was not losing kids, but the connection."

"Menopause felt like I was saying good-bye to children."

For some of us, motherhood is one—and sometimes the only—area in which we experience intense connection with another human being. Fertility allowed access to the most profound bond we had ever felt. With menopause that access had ended, or soon would end. And we could never experience it *in the same way* again.

If neither we nor our family are aware that we are undergoing identity or role changes with menopause, the result can be confusing and problematic for everyone.

"I had put a lot of my energies into being a mother, and being, you know, housewife, and all that sort of stuff. Menopause was a signal to me that that part of my life was over. When I was finished with menopause I was ready to move on. The *unfairness* I felt was that I did *not* get support from my family in doing this. They were all very comfortable with me being there, performing as usual. And I knew my job in that way was finished. But nobody was willing to let me go. What I wanted was some attention to me, the person, who hadn't been there for a long time. Who had, sort of, been pushed aside because I had been a role for such a long time. And now I was going to be more of a separate individual. But my family was not ready to think of me that way."

Doris Lessing echoes these sentiments in her novel, *The Summer Before the Dark*. For her central character, "the light that was the desire to please had gone out."[66] The experiences of the women are filled with references to how they or other women in and past menopause "suddenly" lost the desire to please or nurture *in the way they had before*.

> "My grandmother stopped nurturing when she went through menopause and my mother had to take over in the family. I asked my mother what happened to my grandmother. She said, 'She went through The Change.' Isn't that interesting? That's more of a change than we usually think about with menopause!"

> "I remember wanting to get up from the table and thinking, 'I do not want to be with these people [husband and children]. I want to be away from them.' Actually, it was more that I wanted to get away from *how* they were seeing me—because they weren't seeing *me*. Those thoughts scared me because I didn't understand them. And I certainly didn't feel comfortable telling anybody about them."

> "My aunt had been looking after everybody all her life, near as I could tell. She was *famous* for it. I remember everyone was so shocked because she just *stopped* looking after everybody. And when she stopped it caused a scandal in the whole family. I remember hearing my mother (who was younger than my aunt) saying to her friend that it was because of menopause. That she'd just got fed up with doing it and had had enough."

"I realized that I didn't want to look after my husband or my children any more. That doesn't mean that I don't love them or want to be with them. I just needed to be with them in a different way. I have changed. My relationship with my husband and kids needed to change too. And that *was not easy*, I can tell you. Especially when I barely knew what was different myself."

These women were ready to break out of old roles and identities. They felt different, yet often could not explain this to others. Nor were their changes recognized by those around them. In some ways, this is not surprising because, as women, we tend to be negatively judged when we stop doing the nurturing others have come to expect from us and which is required under the laws of "femininity."

Given the meanings attached to what we are leaving behind, menopause may provide many of us with greater opportunity to be recognized as persons beyond socially-influenced identity and roles. To be sure, all of us want this throughout our lives: to be seen and valued for who we are despite the cloaks we may put on to satisfy societal standards. Unfortunately, many years may go by before we have the opportunity to experience this freedom.

Finding Our Voices

A majority of the women spoke in various ways of "finding their voice" after menopause. They felt less inhibition or fear about speaking their minds once they moved beyond the laws of "femininity." Some of the vulnerability which accompanies mainstream ideas of femininity had disappeared. And many were able to retrieve some of power they had felt before adolescence. This is not to say that they magically became someone visibly different from who they had been before—rather it was more that they noticed subtle, yet significant, inner changes in themselves.

Male voices are generally characterized as having qualities which include assertiveness, strength, confidence and power. Our female voices, by contrast, have been found to be more tentative, emotional and subjective, often including apology, self-blame and hesitancy.[67] While men may try to talk as if they are bigger than they actually are, many of us tend to talk as if we are smaller.[68] As Susan Brownmiller notes, "even when a woman is a forthright, assertive, highly confident and successful performer on the stage of life, she may temper her speech patterns to fit a less challenging mode."[69] A study of academic women found that even those in positions of authority continue to restrain their voices and inhibit their own questioning, challenging and criticizing.[70] Challenge, other than sexual, risks various "unfeminine" labels. While competence masculinizes the male, it de-feminizes the female.

Carol Gilligan in, *Making Connections,* describes early adolescence as the "meeting place of girls and women." It is here that the self-concepts of girls come in contact with the images of beauty by which females are defined in our culture.[71] And these images of beauty and "femininity" require a certain toning down and modifying of their *female* voice—that is, of their knowledge of the world from a female perspective. Gilligan notes that "adolescence seems a watershed in female development....a time when girls are in danger of losing their voices."[72]

This phenomena is demonstrated in a case study by Rose Desrochers:

"[As she neared] puberty, Maggi discussed experiencing 'a complete reversal' in terms of her voice. 'I got quiet.... I was quite an extravert until I hit about twelve or thirteen and started going through puberty. And then I became very shy and insecure about myself.... because of the physical changes that were happening to me, and I wasn't comfortable with that."[73]

Desrochers notes, "for Maggi, early adolescence ....was a time of narrowing, of limitations. Maggi described going 'into a little shell' and not expressing herself through voice. She described becoming quiet....'unlike' herself; a response to powerful adolescent norms at the time."[74] A girl such as Maggi will turn against the feminine in herself when masculine qualities and values are most prized in a culture.[75]

Carol Gilligan's research indicates that adolescent girls repress and hide what they know and think in a way boys do not. For many of us, this too often marks the beginning of a lifetime of unexpressed—and, thus, hidden—experience and knowledge. In the lives of many adult women, the struggle to "find our voice" and to value it when we find it has been shown to entail a journey backward to the beginning of adolescence. It is, as Gilligan notes, a journey to retrieve our twelve-year-old self, a journey linked with a recovery of voice.[76] A friend of mine experienced this as a need to integrate her 12 year old strength with womanly power. Emily Hancock, in her book, *The Girl Within* writes that the women she interviewed felt distress when they realized that "the task of a woman's lifetime boils down to reclaiming the authentic identity she'd embodied as a girl."[77]

On the eve of impending breast surgery, the poet, Audre Lorde, found herself intensely aware of the significance of voice and silence in her life:

"In becoming forcibly and essentially aware of my mortality. . . .what I most regretted were my silences. Of what had I *ever* been afraid?. . . .Death, on the other hand, is the final silence. And that might be coming quickly, now, without regard for whether I had ever spoken what needed to be said, or had only betrayed myself into small silences, while I planned someday to speak, or waited for someone else's words. And I began to recognize a source of power within myself that comes from the knowledge that while it is most desirable not to be afraid, learning to put fear into a perspective gave me great strength."[78]

Some of the women had an approximation of this experience once past menopause and feeling freedom from the meanings the dominant culture associates with fertility.

"I've been taking evening university classes off and on for years. I used to always just listen and hardly ever question what was going on. Now I question and argue all over the place! I just don't care as much what anyone thinks of me. I speak my own thoughts a lot more now. I used to censor them a lot, especially depending on who I was with. More if I was with a man than with a woman."

"I'm a lot more 'no nonsense' now. Frankly, I feel as though I wasted a lot of years where my mind just didn't get the exercise it was capable of. I shut myself down a lot. Actually, I'm really sad about that. Seems a real waste."

"I don't watch what I say as much as I used to. And I can't remember doing that since I was a kid."

Freedom in "Invisibility"

The women realized that there was an unexpected freedom that came with being postmenopausal. This was, however a double-edged freedom—one which can be as distressing as it is freeing. The distress relates to feeling invisible as a sexual person and as a person with value-as-a-Woman.

Charles Simmons, writing for a male audience, notes:

"You realize that all your life you have screened women out. Too tall, too short, too fat, too thin, ill dressed ....And of course, too mature. The gray hair, the dowager's hump, the stringy arms, you didn't have to look actually, not to be interested. A hint in the eye's corner kept the eye moving for the fresh face, the springy hair, the youthful waist between firm hips and bust."[79]

As women, when we or others consider us to be "over the hill" we essentially disappear from the general view. Many of us can feel invisible when we sense that our womanhood has lost value in the eyes of our culture. Unless those of us who are postmenopausal woman can appear to defy the process of aging (as advertisements and magazine articles consistently urge us to do), the media tends to ignore us as still-vibrant, sexual, capable and useful women.

While it is clearly distressing not to feel "seen"— particularly if you have a history of being noticed—it does bring benefits. "Invisibility" allows us certain freedoms to behave and dress as we wish.

"In that realm I've got nothing to lose now. So I do what I please more than I ever have before."

"Now that menopause is behind me, I feel like a different woman. I have always felt closer to women than to men, so I've decided to express my sexuality where my intimacy is: with another woman."

"I feel far more adventuresome and much more willing to 'step out' than I ever have before."

"Now that I finally have the courage to *enjoy* my sexuality, it's less socially-acceptable to *flaunt* it, but I go ahead and do it anyway. I spent a lifetime not enjoying my femaleness and it feels like high time that I began."

As postmenopausal women, many of us have uncovered a new-found adventurousness and willingness to explore where we would have hesitated before. We may feel more able to break through previous assumptions, standards or beliefs, thus opening up a new range of possibilities for ourselves. We often feel less inhibited about trying new experiences; some feel safer from sexual harassment; and some feel more freedom from social customs which, previously, may have stood in the way of something we wanted to do.

More Stability and Security

Transitions such as menopause are usually the more turbulent times of our lives because we're adjusting to change of one kind or another. Once through menopause, the women felt a shift toward feeling more stable and secure in themselves. Janine O'Leary Cobb sums it up in this way in her menopause newsletter, *A Friend Indeed*, "Most [physical symptoms] will disappear or be incorporated into a new and stable sense of self once the body has adjusted to a non-reproductive state."[80]

12
Menopause as a Rite of Passage

A rite of passage marks a transition and has particular implications for our self development and our relationship to society. Victor Turner, an authority on rites of passage, writes that whereas a transition is a process, or a becoming, *a rite of passage is often a transformation*.[81] He uses the analogy of a pupa changing from grub to moth. This is reminiscent of the metaphor of a chrysalis used by one of the woman when asked to describe her experience of menopause.

Arnold van Gennep, author of a classic book on rites of passage, spent years travelling around the world researching this phenomena. He demonstrated that all rites of passage, regardless of the culture in which they appear have three phases: (1) ending: a separation whereby we enter a status which differs from the one we held before; (2) a period of instability: we, or the group to which we belong, pass through an unstable time in which we feel cut off from who we were— and, in terms of our identity—being in a "no-man's land;" (3) emergence: the passage is completed; we are stable once more, having experienced a certain transformation of identity and status in the community.[82] These phases often blur into one another rather than being sharply distinct. For the women who felt their menopause was on time, their experiences have a remarkable correspondence with these phases.

An ending, a separation:

The women were ending fertility and all it meant to them and in their culture. Also ending was an average of 35 years of menstrual cycles which had served as a significant marker of the passage of time. As a result, they experienced an enforced separation from the group they had previously belonged to: the Menstruating Women Group.

A period of instability, cut off from previous identity, betwixt and between:

During menopause the women experienced mood swings, confusion, uncertainty and vulnerability in connection with their sense of identity as women. Much of that time was characterized by feeling disconnected from who they had been, as women.

"I just kept saying to my husband, this woman you're looking at now isn't me. It just isn't me."

"I didn't know who I was. Half the time I felt like I was losing my femaleness."

"Sometimes I worried that I was becoming masculine."

Emergence:

Once out of menopause the women spoke of "emerging," of having "come through" and of "feeling released." They felt more stable and secure than they had during menopause. Parts of their identity-as-a-woman and their status in their culture had undergone a change.

When we consider menopause as a developmental transition and rite of passage, it begins to look quite different from the ways in which we have conventionally looked at it. This new perspective has significant implications in terms of how we think about menopause and menopausal women.

Catalyst for Personal Change

"I became more aware of another side of myself....I think menopause made me look at certain things. Now, I don't know if this happens because you're very vulnerable at that time or what. Maybe you feel you've lost a lot of attractiveness and have to start looking at what you have left. I don't know exactly how the process works, but it's something like that for me."

"I have felt more vulnerable and self-critical during menopause than at any other time in my life. It feels as though it has to end up with me valuing myself—whatever the external standards I'm so aware of."

"I'm not sure why, but I ended up working through a lot of personal stuff from childhood and around my relationship with my husband during those menopause years. Doing that was connected somehow with my going through menopause."

"I really feel a change in me now the menopause is over. And that's called for a bunch of re-negotiations with my family."

Events which are significant in our lives can often stimulate self-examination, reflection and re-evaluation. Some typical examples are the birth or death of a loved one, marriage, job loss or a promotion. These often give us a different perspective on ourselves and allow us to reconsider ourselves and others. Conflict or distress can often promote self growth. For many of us, menopause acts as a catalyst for self-examination, personal change and the uncovering of latent talents.

Doors to Creativity

Many of the women past menopause reported that they felt creative in more ways than they had before. For some this was because they felt less afraid of exploring, taking a chance or risking judgement. Somehow, this isn't surprising because it brings to mind the often-heard comment of women in and past menopause: "I've got nothing to lose now that I'm over the hill!"

Those who have studied creativity note that it is found in all healthy children and often becomes harder to access as we grow up.[83] Creativity can be blocked by the need to "play it safe," and by lack of social support or encouragement.

A number of factors have an influence on our creative potential. Among them are freedom from rigidly-defined roles, freedom from feeling a need to control our speech and behavior, and freedom from feeling a need to conform. Particularly significant is a sense of permission to be ourselves.[84] For many of us, these criteria are met once we have left menopause—and all that it means—behind.

* * * * * * * * * * *

The language of development ran through the women's stories of their menopause. Given that all of us go through menopause, and given the cultural importance attached to fertility, it would seem natural to expect menopause to have developmental significance in our lives.

Menopause may bring about a phase of development regardless of the chronological age at which it arrives. As Judith Stevens-Long in *Adult Development* points out, "some people expand their goals and behaviors when they encounter enforced change, substituting new roles and relationships for old ones."[85] And, as Janine O'Leary Cobb notes, the upheavals of menopause may be a healthy sign of a desire to go in a different direction.[86]

The women who had completed menopause felt as though they were on the threshold of a new phase in their lives as women. Although not without their concerns for the future, they had a certain optimism which many of them hadn't had before. As women who had gone through "The Change," they often felt stronger, more alert, competent, vibrant and sensual than they had ever imagined they would be. *These women were unanimous in pointing out that this was largely because they had had the opportunity to tell their stories and to hear those of other women.* As a result, they felt less alone, more "normal" and more confident than they had been before.

When women set aside what they feel they should

experience and begin to talk about their deepest feelings,

much of what they have assumed about themselves

collapses.

13
Re-visiting the Negative Stereotype of the Menopausal Woman

The negative stereotype of the menopausal woman is that of a woman who seems to have lost her sexuality and who appears to be angry, depressed and stressed. I believe that if we look at her more closely and assume she has these feelings for a good reason, how she is feeling begins to make a lot of sense. Whether this "menopausal woman" is the exception or the rule, she also warrants this closer look because minorities—like stereotypes—can serve as mirrors, giving us the opportunity to catch glimpses of parts of ourselves. In this way, we can gain a greater understanding of those times when we feel just like the negative stereotype.

Learning From Those Who Have a Difficult Menopause

There is a widespread tendency to discount, devalue or ignore the experiences of those of us who have a difficult time with menopause. The consensus seems to be that we are in the minority and, therefore have no place in the discussion of "normal" menopause. However, menopause experiences range over a continuum and differ more in degree than in kind. As such, the midrange is a mixture of both extremes. Given menopause's history of taboo and silence in our majority culture, it makes sense that by paying attention to the experiences of women at the troublesome-menopause extreme we can gain a clearer picture of the average experience. Women who have experienced the troublesome extreme are the ones who feel the effects of the stereotype most strongly. Therefore, we have much we can learn from them. Throughout history, a function of fringe groups and minorities has been to provide us with perspectives on the general culture—views often too difficult to see when we are part of the majority.

When we have feelings which are difficult to sort out, they can often be made clearer by learning from those who have had an extreme version of those feelings. The "larger than life" quality of their experience can help us to clarify our own. These others, having been propelled by either the power of their emotion or the severity of their situation, are often able to put words to what they—and we to a lesser degree—are feeling. *Women who have a difficult menopause may be giving voice to experiences and feelings about which many of us stay silent.*

The tendency to discount the stereotypically "menopausal" woman is a subtle theme running through most of the discussions on menopause. And it is an attitude which seems to be accepted by most professionals. The implication is that only a small group of particular women are prone to difficulty with menopause (particularly of the emotional variety). Falling into this group are those of us who feel our main asset was our appearance or sexuality, as well as those of us who have low self esteem or esteem which is tied to our roles as mothers or wives. This assumption ignores the fact that *most* of us share these characteristics to some extent. And this assumption contributes to a belief many of us have that other women do not have the same emotions or experiences as we do. Instead, we need to recognize that during menopause majority culture taboos and stereotypes to some degree influence *all of us* in that culture. And all of us will go through some form of change of *self* as a result of menopause. Some of us will be more aware of this change than others. And some will have more of a need to understand this change than others.

Any of us who suffer discomfort or pain with menopause have a right to have these problems taken seriously. All possibilities for relief should be made available to us. Although, as women, many of us have remarkable capacities to endure pain, we were not born to suffer or to be masochists. While I have no doubt that much of women's distress at menopause is caused by dominant-culture attitudes, that is certainly not the whole picture. No matter how dramatically attitudes change, a percentage of us will have a difficult time with the physical changes of menopause. And we must always keep in mind that all of our experiences of menopause consist of physical, emotional, social, cultural,

genetic, life style and environmental factors—in fluctu-
ating and complex interaction.

Anger

The stereotypical "menopausal woman" is suspected
of, or shows signs of anger. Here is a woman who,
at least for the moment, has clearly thrown caution
and "femininity" to the wind. She is not calm, contained
or controlled—in fact, she epitomizes lack of control.
Regardless of any beauty or charm she may possess
at other times, she is seen in that moment as unattractive
—and usually judges herself to be this way. Of all the
emotions, anger gets the label, "ugly." If we trust that
this stereotype is there for a reason, the next step is
to ask: Why would we be angry during menopause?

As we have seen, there are many reasons for this
anger. Yet, anger is so opposite to the feminine ideal
that it can be frightening, both for ourselves while we
experience it, and for those witnessing our anger. For
many of us, expressing anger puts us in danger of being
scorned, labelled or physically harmed should we "go
too far." The English language has many negative labels
for us when we are angry: "bitch," "hag," "man-hater,"
"shrew," "cow," "old bat," "nag." In contrast, it has none
for the angry man. As women, we can often fear opening
the door to the sources of our anger, believing that
if we do we may remain angry forever—and, therefore,
unfeminine and unlovable. And fear of losing connections with loved ones may contribute to our keeping
any anger we may feel to ourselves. For all these reasons,
the *power* of straight-forward, clearly understood anger
becomes *impotent* because the emotion itself feels
threatening.

Anger is often listed as a symptom in the Premenstrual

Syndrome (PMS). Anger—or frustration, irritability or hysteria—is also part of the menopausal stereotype. Emily Martin's comments on anger and PMS in *The Woman in the Body* offer us a perspective on the anger the women felt during their menopause:

> "The reason anger expressed by women is problematic in our society is that anger (and allied feelings such as irritability) makes it hard for a woman to carry out her expected role of maintaining harmonious relationships within the family. . . . Her own anger, however substantial the basis for it, must not be allowed to make life hard on those around her. If she has an anger she cannot control, she is considered hormonally unbalanced and should seek medical treatment for her malfunction. If she goes on subjecting her family to such feelings, disastrous consequences— construed as a woman's *fault* in the PMS literature— may follow."[87]

It may be that our periods, and our menopause, are times of truth when allowing anger to surface feels safer because it can be attributed to a female condition or illness. Those of us who have felt full of rage at times during menopause may not understand *why*, and, therefore, assume we are suffering from "raging hormones." The popular view has falling levels of estrogen responsible for this situation. And I have no doubt that there is an interaction going on. However, as we have seen, there are powerful meanings associated with menopause in the majority culture—meanings about which we have every right to be angry.

For the women quoted in this book, anger was a theme

on two levels: that which occurred *during* menopause, and anger *generated* during the process of exploring their menopause and hearing the experiences of other women. This generated-anger is what emerges from the development of a broader perspective, when we *realize we have something to be angry about*. It relates to becoming personally aware of the discomfort and damage brought about by the *menstrual taboo*, the *negative stereotype* of the menopausal women and *the ways in which women are devalued*.

Grief

Many of the women's emotions during menopause fit with feelings associated with the grief process: sadness, anger at feeling helpless, guilt, anxiety, loneliness, fatigue, shock, numbness and yearning.[88] In addition, various physical sensations, thought processes and behaviors associated with grief are experienced by many of us during menopause: tightness in chest and throat, heightened sensitivity to noise, breathlessness, weakness in the muscles, lack of energy, dry mouth, confusion, preoccupation, sleep disturbances, absent-minded behavior and crying.

I am not suggesting that grief is a central emotion for most of us during menopause or that grief causes menopausal symptoms. However, I don't think we should ignore or discount the element of grief. It is one of the many variables which have yet to be seriously figured into the menopause equation for those of us in the majority culture. The last time many of us experienced such combined physiological and emotional change was during pregnancy—where the outcome was a child, most often a joyous occasion. Rarely is the outcome of menopause associated with joy. Rather, menopause signals entrance to a stage of life that *seems* to have few messages conveying success, pleasure and health, so it is normal to grieve what *seems* to be left behind.

Depression

As women, we are not *inevitably* depressed at menopause or at any other stage in our reproductive life cycle. Too often, we ignore possible social-cultural explanations for depression in women, and too readily either blame their hormones or assume a woman is neurotic, masochistic, or weak. Instead, explanations for depression in women are *more likely* to be found outside ourselves: in our individual life situation or in the way we are treated or viewed within our culture.[89] Accordingly, I believe we need to change the way we look at the depressive syndromes associated with our reproductive life cycle: "premenstrual syndrome," "postnatal depression" and the "menopausal syndrome." They can just as easily be seen as natural (survival) reactions to the physiological changes in combination with the countless ways in which our experiences *as women,* tend to be misrepresented and misunderstood within the majority culture.

Many of us tend to assume that depression in women which does not have an *obvious* external cause must be caused by a hormonal or chemical imbalance. Possible social-cultural causes are often ignored because it can be difficult to see the forest when you are one of the trees. In trying to understand behavior, our majority culture still tends to look to individual psychological factors and much less to social factors. One of the consequences of this tendency is that many of us continue to believe that other women do not feel the way we feel. Then we are easily vulnerable to believing that there is something wrong with us. I believe it is for social—not hormonal—reasons that depression is more common in women than in men.

The time has come to understand aspects of depression in a different way. It is important to see depressed people as *demoralized* people making a statement about the circumstances in which they find themselves.[90]

Identity as a person, our sense of self, is deeply rooted to our gender: to our maleness or femaleness. How we feel about ourselves as a woman plays a central role in our level of self esteem. And as evidenced by the experiences of the women I have worked with, the way many of us feel about ourselves as women is affected and changed during menopause.

The U.S. National Institute of Mental Health conducted a poll of hundreds of patients with severe clinical depression and listed in order of importance the top ten triggers of depression. Topping the list was a threat to sexual identity: a real or imagined threat to, or loss of, masculinity or femininity. Also listed in the top ten were instability, uncertainty and shift in social status.[91] Given the existing majority culture climate in which most of us go through menopause, some form of depression begins to look like a *normal* response. In addition, depression that does not have a clear source or explanation will often show up as a physical "symptom."

Elissa Melamed, in her book, *Mirror, Mirror: The Terror of Not Being Young,* points out that most of us have some sense of the wide-ranging impact castration or emasculation would have on a man. I would add that we have not considered the impact on us of the changes in identity and the changes in value-as-a-woman which can occur as a result of going through menopause in our dominant culture. When we are involuntarily de-feminized, our life force and sexual energy (libido), along with our effectiveness and emotional and physical well-being are all affected.

Feeling invisible is another understandable source of depression. If we feel that who we are or what we do is not *seen* by others, we can expect to feel devalued. Many of our experiences with invisibility are not unique to menopause. For example, "women's work" is "invisible" work because it is rarely given the value, significance and importance of "men's work." Included in "women's work" are the myriad of largely unnamed (and therefore unrecognized) background tasks many of us perform in our various relationships: child rearing; food preparation and service; maintenance of the home; selection and care of clothing; responsibility for birthdays, anniversaries, celebrations and times of ritual important to reaffirming family and friendship bonds; maintaining connections and harmony between family members; and looking after the emotional needs of others. This is to name only a few of the unacknowledged jobs most of us do. This invisibility about these parts of our lives can be difficult to talk about because we don't have a history of doing so. This lack of acknowledgement and silence only deepens our potential for depression.

14
Stress and Menopause

All the reproductive stages in our lives (of which menopause is one) come associated with particular stresses. As this stress does not usually have an *acceptable* or *easily identified* source, it is often attributed to what is happening in our body and is called an illness or a syndrome.[92]

The physiological changes, coupled with the cultural meanings attached to menopause, are ample cause for stress. It would be reasonable, then, to *expect* signs of stress to appear in physical or emotional forms for those of us in menopause in the majority culture.

Responses to stress can be profuse sweating, strong body odor, skin disturbances such as rashes or pimples, confusion, memory lapses and experiences of the "mind going blank." These are experiences many of us have during menopause. It may be that researchers will eventually come up with more detailed physiological explanations for the physical ailments many of us feel during menopause. However, in the meantime, many of these experiences can also be explained by the highly distressful dynamics which surround going through menopause in the majority culture.

Although our hormonal systems are changing because of menopause, hormones may also *be influenced by the stress associated with the meanings of menopause in mainstream society*. As a testament to the power of stress to affect our hormonal system, recall that some women's periods stop when they experience severe stress. The hormones involved in starting and stopping menstruation are regulated by the pituitary gland, which in turn is controlled by the hypothalamus and other higher brain centers. The hypothalamus is intimately related to the emotions.[93] This is not to say that stress causes menopausal ailments, but it most certainly plays a role in *how we experience menopause*.

Some additional reactions to stress can include:

- headaches
- neck, back and shoulder pains
- nervous twitches
- trouble sleeping or early morning waking
- greater susceptibility to colds, influenza or other illnesses
- worsening of existing conditions or illnesses
- depression, anxiety, irritability, nervousness
- jaw pains and toothaches (from grinding teeth)
- cankers, cold sores
- stomach aches, diarrhea, loss of or increase in appetite.[94]

It is significant to remember that *stress increases when the source of the stress is not clear* or easy to pinpoint. This is often the case with menopause.

Stress is about how we respond to our physical and social-cultural environment. Until the late 1970s, the medical community believed that, although the brain processed sensations and thoughts and controlled body movement, it couldn't directly affect other parts of the body, such as the endocrine, immune and autonomic nervous systems. Before then, there was no scientific explanation for the bodily changes reported by people who practised meditation or yoga, or who were given hypnotherapy. Today, research from the field of psychoneuroimmunology (PNI) is providing some of the answers. What researchers are recognizing is that there is a link between our minds, our emotions and the functioning of our bodies. Information from this field about the effects of emotional stress and various emotional states on our hormonal and immune systems is rapidly accumulating. Award winning biochemist, Dr. Candace Pert, for example, was one of the first researchers to show that the body produces its own opiate-like chemicals which can reduce pain. She writes:

"In the beginning of my work, I matter-of-factly presumed that emotions were in the head or the brain. Now I would say that they are really in the body as well. They are expressed in the body and are part of the body. I can no longer make a strong distinction between the brain and the body."[95]

Communication between our mind and our body— and our body feeding back to our mind—is dependent on communication via our immune system, our autonomic nervous system, and our endocrine (hormonal) system, all "talking to each other" in a harmonious fashion. All three systems use "messenger molecules" called neuropeptides (for example, endorphins) to communicate within themselves and with each other. Neuropeptides are transmitted through virtually all the fluids in our bodies, including blood and lymph, as well as between brain cells (neurons). Some of the many biological effects attributed to our neuropeptides are the specific release of hypothalamic or pituitary hormones, stress responses, memory and temperature regulation. When we become distressed, our hormonal responses are affected. For example, those of us who have charted our hot flashes often note that we find they increase during situations where we are nervous or under stress.[96]

Our emotional state and level of stress are not separate from our body, including our menopause. At the same time, it is important to watch for some of the dangers in the idea that "we create our own reality." For some of us, there is a certain amount of shame which can come with the idea that if we are sick—or have a hard time with menopause—we have *caused* it to happen to ourselves. From this perspective, those of us having physical treatments, such as taking hormones, can feel this as a weakness, or we may believe that we *should* be able to overcome our ailments through mental or spiritual means. A very cruel extension of this view occurs when otherwise well-meaning people ask a sufferer what she is trying to teach herself by being sick. The implication is that a psychological or spiritual weakness is the cause of the problem.

Ken Wilber, a well known philosopher/theorist, realized that he had to re-think some of the mind-body concepts he had once held. He offers what I think is very good advice that we can apply to menopause. He was asked what he would advise if we came to him in distress with some physical problems. He replied that, in general, he would advise us to start at the physical level and to ensure all is well there. If that checks out, then

explore whether or not an emotional state is the cause
of the problem. If nothing materializes on that level,
examine the spiritual level because looking after our
health requires that we meet our needs on all three
levels. Wilber cautions that if we go even one level too
high in suggesting the cause of the problem, we run
the risk of generating a certain moral guilt in the person.[97]
This form of guilt can be destructive. As Wilber notes,
"in our Judeo-Christian culture, with its pervasive
emphasis on guilt and blame, illness too often is seen
as punishment for wrongdoing."[98]

I suspect that this harmful moralistic guilt plays a
role in the reluctance some of us feel about revealing
that we are on hormone therapy. The only sane and
kind approach to menopause is one which recognizes
the complexity of the topic and the individuality of
each of our experiences, and which recognizes that
menopause is a significant bodily (hormonal) change,
as well as a significant personal and social-cultural
transition.

Connections Between "Unfinished Business," Menopause and Stress

For some of us the experience of menopause triggers
unhappy or traumatic memories. The same can be true
for our experiences of pregnancy, labor, childbirth,
miscarriage, abortion, stillbirth, as well as our attempts
to become pregnant or to avoid it. Any emotionally
unresolved issue relating to our feelings of value-as-a-
woman, femininity or sexuality may surface amidst the
changes and meanings of menopause. Or, if we feel
out of control, we may find ourselves with memories
or sensations relating to other times in our lives when
we/our body or our environment felt out of control,

even if they were for totally different reasons. At the best of times, this experience can be confusing and frightening for us. It can feel more confusing to us if there doesn't appear to be any good reason for these feelings to have surfaced at this time. Common experiences many of us share are of sexual abuse in childhood or traumatic experiences related to pregnancy, abortion, miscarriage and labor.

Because menopause involves some loss, it has the potential to bring to the surface any of our memories of past losses, large and small. Those of us who have never fully mourned the death of a loved one, the ending of a relationship, an abortion, a miscarriage, stillbirth, or any other significant loss may find that feelings and memories of it surface, especially during the early years of our menopause. In addition, because menopause signals the end of youth, those of us who feel we never really had a childhood may find ourselves deeply grieving the loss of our youth. Again, because this process is not commonly understood, these feelings can be frightening and confusing. Our levels of stress rise when the source of the stress is unclear and "emotional flashbacks" can be intense, to the point where a qualified therapist or counsellor is needed to sort out the memories that menopause may be triggering.

15
Menopause From a Medical Perspective

Throughout history, we have been affected in one way or another by medical and scientific views of the workings of our female bodies.[99] How we talk and feel about what goes on in our bodies is strongly influenced by the medical community.[100] Medicine is the source of our most popular views of menopause, views conveyed in the language it uses to discuss and describe menopause. These medical perceptions are deeply entrenched in our dominant culture and history, and they influence all of us on some level. Descriptions of menopause which come from medical professionals play a role, both directly and indirectly, in shaping the environment in which most of us in North America experience menopause. These descriptions, therefore, warrant a closer look.

It is easy to dismiss the impact of the language we, or others, use to describe us. However, words in the form of labels or descriptions are potentially very harmful and this is particularly true if the ones who say them have social power. For example, many of us will have been seriously affected if, in childhood, people in power or authority suggested there was something wrong with us. The medical community is popularly viewed as having considerable power and authority with respect to our bodies and our health. The words used by this community to describe and talk about our bodies and their functions are words most of us have lived with. These words strongly influence how most of us feel about our bodies/ourselves and our physical processes.

Many of us receive information about menopause from our physicians. This information is either conveyed directly to us by our physician or indirectly through material available in his or her office. A current and widely available example is *Managing Menopause*, a booklet published by Ayerst Laboratories, the leading manufacturer of a prescription estrogen. In it, menopause is described as our *failure* to ovulate because of a *decrease* in estrogen production, resulting in an *insufficient* supply of this hormone. A serious *complication* of our *insufficiency* is seen as the development of osteoporosis, which is described as a significant problem and risk for menopausal women. The authors question whether it is normal for us to spend 30 or more of our post-menopausal years experiencing low estrogen levels. They suggest that estrogen therapy is available to alleviate— directly or indirectly—menopausal experiences of hot flushes, psychological "symptoms," osteoporosis, cardiovascular problems and genitourinary tract problems.

Another way to learn about the perspectives of the medical profession is to examine the college and medical texts used to educate physicians and nurses. Emily Martin in *The Woman In the Body*, did so in order to determine the nature of the language used to describe female reproductive processes (including menopause). She notes that a "signal-response metaphor was found almost universally in current texts for premedical and medical students." This is a "communication system organized hierarchically, not a committee reaching decisions by mutual influence."[101]

Menstruation is discussed as a case of *failed production* because reproduction did not occur. Martin points out that while no reputable scientist would talk about menstruation as pathological, descriptions of menstruation in these texts indicate that it is regarded as such. She cites the following example taken from a currently used college text: "In rapid succession the reader is confronted with 'degenerate,' 'decline,' 'withdrawn,' 'spasms,' 'lack,' 'weakened,' 'leak,' 'deteriorate,' 'discharge,' and, after all that, 'repair.'"[102] These are not neutral terms. Rather, they convey a sense either of failure, breakdown or of something going wrong.

Martin adds:

"One response to my argument would be that menstruation just is in some objective sense a process of breakdown and deterioration. The particular words are chosen to describe it because they best fit the reality of what is happening. My counterargument is to look at other processes in the body that are fundamentally analogous to menstruation in that they involve the shedding of a lining to see whether they also are described in terms of breakdown and deterioration."[103]

She examined literature on stomach linings (a gender neutral topic) and male ejaculate and found the descriptive language to be very different. Rather than words of decay and breakdown in need of repair, the emphasis is on *production* of mucus and the periodic *renewal* of the lining.[104]

What applies to menstruation once a month applies to menopause once in every lifetime. Part of the current imagery attached to menopause is that of a *breakdown of central control,* another aspect of failed production.[105] The message is that our reproductive organs *fail* to produce *enough* estrogen, a state *harmful* to our health.

The authors of a 1988 second edition of a standard menopause reference text for physicians describe it as covering "the comprehensive management of women during years when reproductive hormone activity fades."[106] In it, menopause is discussed in terms of hormonal loss, declining reproductive capacity and reproductive failure and loss. Reference is made to the "pathophysiology" of menopause, and to both menopause and aging as "conditions."[107]

Menopause is often viewed by the medical profession in terms of the health hazards associated with it. Currently, as indicated in the *Merck Manual,* the major health hazards associated with menopause are osteoporosis and coronary heart disease, with extended estrogen therapy recommended for its prevention.[108] However, questions remain within the medical community as to the safety of estrogen use. In 1990, an editorial on osteoporosis in the *Journal of the American Medical Association,* notes that "the question of appropriateness of use of estrogens continues to be controversial."[109] Another editorial in the October 14, 1993, *New England Journal of Medicine,* notes that "the reduction in the risk of hip fracture associated with estrogen treatment dissipates after treatment." The authors add that "physicians and postmenopausal women should recognize that osteoporosis is unlikely to be prevented by taking estrogen for just a decade or so after menopause."[110]

Given the influence the medical community has on our views of health and disease, most of us will naturally be affected by our physician's attitude toward menopause. Some doctors trivialize or dismiss women's complaints about menopause by telling them to keep busy and have a sense of humor. Some others have a tendency to prescribe hormone therapy for most, if not all, of their menopausal patients. And it is not uncommon for women to feel rushed by their doctors, hesitating to take up the doctor's time with "silly" questions, yet not knowing where else to turn for answers.[111]

While there are always exceptions (some of whom I know personally), I believe that the majority of the medical community does, in fact, view menopause as a disease. As Jerilynn Prior, an endocrinologist, concludes in her article, "One Voice On Menopause," in the *Journal of the American Medical Women's Association*, most physicians unfortunately still view menopause as an estrogen deficiency disease which must be treated with estrogen.[112] Although few physicians would say—or perhaps even believe—that they consider menopause a disease, how they approach, talk about and treat menopause suggests that they do.

16
Menopause As A Developmental Transition

Looking at menopause in light of what we know about transitions provides us with very different perspectives on the experience. William Bridges based his book, *Transitions: Making Sense of Life's Changes*, on extensive research into rites of passage and transitions by anthropologists such as Victor Turner, Arnold van Gennep and Mircea Eliade. Bridges notes that transitions are key times in the natural process of self-renewal.

He cites the following as some characteristics of transitions in general:

1. When the ending which begins a transition is not named and processed *as an ending,* successful movement through the transition is hampered. For example, feelings of sadness cannot be overcome and laid to rest until we identify the loss behind the sadness. A free-floating depression can be a consequence of such unidentified endings. Too often, the whole idea of termination violates our mistaken idea that devel-

opment means gain and has nothing to do with loss.

2. What we *bring to* a transition influences how we experience it. Attitudes, expectations, past events, timing and familiarization with the experiences of others all play a role.

3. As in nature, beginnings and endings are linked. The experience of one influences the experience of the other. For example, our experiences with menarche and menstruation will influence our experience of menopause.

4. Feeling disoriented or uncomfortable is a natural part of the process of going through a transition.

5. Part of being in a transition, particularly a life transition, is spending time in a place in between: leaving aspects of who we were, and not yet arrived at who we will become. This is the neutral zone. The desire to be alone, and the feeling of being out of sorts are characteristic of this time.

The parallels to the women's experiences of menopause are clear. Notice how differently menopause *feels* when it is discussed in this way—as a transition.

Nancy Schlossberg has examined transitions in terms of what helps or hinders our movement through them.[113] Although she was not addressing menopause, her findings give us an interesting lens through which to view it. She notes that it is not the transition per se that is critical, but *how much it alters our roles, relationships, routines and assumptions*. As we have seen, all these are potentially influenced by the meanings attached to menopause in our majority culture.

How able we feel to cope with the situation is also significant. Given the extent of what remains unknown about menopause, add the controversy over hormone therapy and the "diseases" menopause is said to bring, and it is not surprising that so many of us feel that we are not coping well.

Schlossberg found that our ability to cope with a transition can be determined by examining certain questions:

- To what extent do we see this transition as positive or negative, expected or unexpected, desired or dreaded, voluntary or imposed?
- Do we have previous experience with a similar transition?
- To what extent do we believe we have options or the power to change the conditions of the transition?
- What is the extent of the support and understanding of family, close friends and co-workers?
- Do we have an understanding of the meaning of this transition in our life?
- What is our ability to creatively cope with the situation?

When we apply these questions to menopause, most of us in the majority culture could be *expected* to have a difficult time with menopause. Rarely is it a welcomed experience. We have no choice about going through it. We don't have previous experience with it. The menstrual taboo, negative stereotype and accompanying silence can isolate many of us from potential sources of support. This isolation can contribute to some of our feelings of not understanding what we are going through. Finally, the personal and cultural meanings of this experience are often obscured.

With menopause we go through considerable physical as well as emotional change. Not surprisingly, we may need time to reflect upon and assimilate what is happening to us. When dealing with teenage transitions, we are usually aware of their need for space and elbow room. Although similar dynamics are operating during menopause, we rarely recognize this need for "time out." Yet, at different times throughout our relationships with our partners, it is natural to want to have privacy and some space to call our own. We need to be able to say *no*, to not feel used and to experience ourselves as separate. These needs are increased when one member of the relationship is in a life transition.

Early Menopause: The Significance of Timing

Whether we feel a transition is on time or not influences how we feel about it and, therefore, how we go through it. For example, girls who are late starting menstruation often feel very much on the outside of a menstruating group.[114]

"In junior high school, I felt so bad I didn't have it, I was left out from all this discussion [about periods and tampons]. I had to keep quiet, I couldn't talk about it. So I felt when I got it, it allowed me to join these discussions. . . . It was all very important, all a part of being a junior in high school."[115]

The influence of timing also applies to menopause. Having an early menopause can be a devastating experience. The unexpectedness, isolation from our peers and general lack of support and information can all make for a very difficult time. Because one of the meanings of menopause is that it signals the loss of youth, some women experience intense grief, feeling they have by-passed what was left of their youth. It is made more stressful by the fact that rarely are the losses of menopause named and verbalized so we can know and understand our emotions. Women who have an early menopause invariably feel their experiences many times more intensely than women who have an "on-time" menopause.

When is our menopause on time or not? Among professionals, an early menopause is currently considered to be before the age of 40. However, on an individual basis, the key seems to be how we *ourselves* feel about the timing of our menopause. For one woman, being postmenopausal at 44 feels just right as this is when she expected it. Another the same age may be shocked and feel caught unawares. Regardless of our age, the likelihood of having an easier time is increased if we *feel* our menopause is on time—if we *feel* everything is "normal".

*How our experiences are described and whether or not
they are valued has a profound influence on how we go
through them.*

17

The Implications
Of How We
View
Menopause

When we think of menopause in terms of symptoms and otherwise approach it as a medical condition or a problem, even when we carefully avoid calling it one, certain assumptions follow. For one, the definition of a symptom is a "change in bodily sensation, function, or appearance that indicates disorder, abnormality, or disease."[116] Talk of symptoms implies that something requires treatment or correction. If menopause is a condition requiring "fixing" for which we turn to physicians, a domino effect is set in motion. When a problem is seen as a medical one, it requires a medical solution. Medical treatment is not usually treatment we can provide for ourselves and, thus, we become dependent on others for diagnosis and treatment.

Physicians who have concerns about prescribing extra hormones can find themselves in a difficult position if we *demand* treatment in some form or another from them. Although many physicians sense that some of our complaints are influenced by other than biological factors, they can be caught in a double bind. They may feel obliged to follow the underlying philosophy of their profession: if there is distress, try to relieve it. Physicians can easily see themselves as professionally obligated to treat menopause so as to enhance the quality of our lives. For some physicians and their patients, this obligation may also extend to considering a future financial burden on the patient and on the taxpayer if they do not act to prevent possible osteoporosis or other diseases.

From a medical view, the cause of difficulties we may have with menopause will most often originate in either our body or our mind as the result of some form of disturbance, breakdown or failure. *This view does not account for the influence on our bodies and emotions of our social-cultural environment, or for what menopause means to us.* Describing menopause in terms of symptoms implies there is something wrong. This in turn suggests that we have lost some aspect of our health. We may then feel betrayed by our body—especially if we have made every effort to maintain our health.

When we focus most on a medical perspective on menopause, we as women, also play a role in determining what gets researched. Then researchers are further encouraged to focus their efforts on improved medications to either eliminate or more safely alleviate symptoms. When we view menopause as a condition or disease, questions of meaning and their influence on us become irrelevant. The most potent method for improving the quality of our lives as menopausal woman then becomes some form of medical treatment—instead of, for example, focusing on altering both our personal and societal values, beliefs and conditions which influence how we feel about menopause.

A frightening possibility for the future is that women who do not seek treatment may be judged to be selfish or foolish. A situation is being created today whereby a subtle message is going out to women that we are somehow *obligated* to take extra hormones in order to stave off the diseases now being linked to menopause. Unless we do so, we may be seen as allowing ourselves to become a burden on medical systems, health plans and taxpayers because we did not seek preventative treatment. For those of us used to feeling guilty, this can become another subtle form of guilt-making. Although this scenario has "big-brother" overtones, it is not so far fetched. For example, as is common practice, a public lecture on menopause given by a physician was supported by slides provided by a leading pharmaceutical company. The slides portrayed menopause as a condition of hormonal imbalance. One of the reasons presented for women to take extra hormones was to reduce the burden on health care systems.

These comments are not meant to suggest that there is no place for physicians or pharmaceuticals in supporting women through menopause. On the contrary, they are often necessary for those of us having severe problems with menopause. However, I have come to believe that there is a serious difficulty when physicians or we, as women, *assume* that most of us require extra hormones to correct what is seen as a hormonal *imbalance*, and therefore a problem with our bodies.

From a *medical* perspective, difficulty with menopause is basically the result of some failure on a physical or psychological level. From a *developmental* perspective, difficulty with menopause may have individual causes, but the social conditions of women in general will also be significant, just as they are with adolescents.

It is interesting to note a study aimed at discovering what emotional or physical concerns were common to females in specific age groups across the life span. Girls in adolescence and women in menopause reported the largest number of concerns. Women past menopause had the least. Among the adolescent girls, "psychological" complaints (tension, for example) were most common, whereas with menopausal women it was physical problems (hot flushes, for example).[117] Despite the mirror-image nature of the physical changes underlying both transitions, I believe the *type* of symptom experienced reflects the *value society places* on each stage. Adolescence is seen—culturally, and therefore individually—as a significant stage of psychological development triggered by physical changes, so the concerns reported were more often psychological in nature. In contrast, menopause is seen as a process of physical deterioration, so the concerns noted and reported were more physical in nature.

When we begin thinking about menopause in terms of *development*, the focus will shift from breakdown to change. When we understand that what we are going through is part of our natural growing and changing as women, we are more likely to feel hope, rather than the despair, which can arise when we think of menopause as a deficiency or degeneration.

When all sides of menopause are recognized as equally significant, the importance of adding new research directions becomes clear. For example, research on adolescents focuses on the interaction between physical changes and emotional, social and cultural influences. Researchers ask questions such as: "What do they need?" "How are they changing?" "How do they see their world?" "How can professionals help?" When menopause is viewed as a natural stage of development, experiences during the menopausal years will be handled in a similar manner. Menopause will be approached as other life transitions are, as an interaction between physical, emotional, social and cultural elements.

Had the women whose voices appear in this book anticipated and understood this transition to be a part of their development as women, I have no doubt that they would have experienced it very differently.

18
The Menopause Business

Frances B. McCrea extensively examined the history of medical attitudes toward menopause from the late 1800s to the present day.[118] She concludes that a relationship between estrogen, menopausal women, and the medical community began in earnest in 1943 when an estrogen extract from the urine of pregnant mares was developed. This estrogen was inexpensive and easy to administer. By the 1960s it was readily available in North America. The benefits of estrogen therapy were being proclaimed as miraculous in a fight against aging.

At that time, a popular book, *Feminine Forever*, heavily influenced the way both women and the medical community perceived menopause. In it, menopause was described as a hormone deficiency disease similar to diabetes and thyroid dysfunction, and also as a malfunction threatening the "feminine essence." The author advised that most women should begin estrogen therapy before menopause, to prevent hot flashes, loss of memory, depression, nervousness, headache, indigestion, backache, and neurosis. Under the threat of such frightening futures for women, many physicians considered that giving extra estrogen was the only sensible route through menopause. A number of prominent U.S. physicians supported the author's claims, advising that the majority of menopausal women were acutely estrogen-deficient and would therefore benefit from estrogen therapy, even if they had no symptoms.

In the late 1970s, the number of prescriptions for estrogen dropped following publicity about increased risks for cancer of the lining of the uterus (endometrial cancer) associated with administering extra estrogen. At that time a warning was included in prescription packets stating that extra estrogen might be injurious to health.[119] By the end of 1976, papers in prominent medical journals linked use of estrogen with the incidence of gall-bladder disease, endometrial and breast cancers and with higher levels of risk factors for coronary disease.[120]

Despite these concerns, use of estrogen rose again in the early 1980s. Grossman & Bart suggest that this rise was because it seemed that estrogen therapy might prevent or retard osteoporosis.[121] Increasing numbers of hysterectomies were also thought to contribute to a rise in estrogen use. In 1986, Berkun estimated that half the women in the U.S.A. would have had a hysterectomy by the time they reached 65.[122]

A further development encouraging use of estrogen came with the introduction of a combined hormone therapy. To reduce the link between cancer and estrogen treatment, a progesterone-like drug was given along with estrogen to prevent estrogen-related endometrial cancer.

It seems clear that hormone therapy has value for women experiencing profound difficulty with menopause. As Paula Weideger notes, it is the best *medical* method available to us so far, and it does address some of our menopausally related concerns. However, it is not the perfect solution to these concerns because its safety still remains very much in question. Even among proponents of hormone therapy, opinions vary as to use of hormones: how should treatment be administered? To what degree and with what implications to a woman's health? Do the benefits out-weigh the risks?

Critics charge that the pharmaceutical industry has consistently minimized the risks of estrogen therapy and combined hormone therapy, while aggressively promoting its benefits. They sharply criticize what they see as the industry's use of scare tactics with respect to the aging process and the diseases they link to menopause.

Kaufert & McKinlay extensively examined the connection between estrogen research and the medical community.[123] They conclude that the growing list of diseases seen to be preventable through hormone therapy implied an obligation on the physician to prescribe estrogen despite the risk of endometrial cancer. They also charge that it is in the interest of the pharmaceutical companies to establish a market in which women would be kept on long-term therapy, regardless of their menopausal symptoms.[124] They conclude that the idea that extra estrogen is beneficial to women's health "has been actively promoted and [is] currently a carefully orchestrated campaign. . . .advocating estrogen as a barrier against osteoporosis."[125]

Many practitioners see hormone therapy as a panacea for menopausal women and their problems.[126] Janine O'Leary Cobb concludes from her extensive work in the field of menopause that "most doctors distrust a woman's ability to sustain the kind of exercise and diet required to stave off osteoporosis, and many believe that *all* women should receive ERT for life, or until accurate screening programs are in place, whichever comes first."[127] Yet, many women report that while they're on hormone therapy they often *forget* to take a pill or use a cream. Cobb makes a very good point when she notes that "forgetting is often a reflection of a deep-seated uneasiness with the whole process."[128] These concerns are often difficult for women to put into words because so much of menopause still remains in the closet.

Implied throughout medical and pharmaceutical literature, including education packets, is that we have a *deficiency* and that we have lost something in need of *replacement*. Such a prospect can induce fear in even the bravest of us. And fear creates fertile territory for the salesman.

19
Hormone Therapy: Choices and Informed Decisions

Many of us are trying to make inform-ed decisions about whether or not to take extra hormones. There are strong arguments for hormone therapy because it has proven to be a valuable aid to many women during menopause. Because it is not without risks, there are also arguments against its use.

I believe that for a decision to be *truly informed*, we must believe we have *real and viable choices*. And we must be able to assess the choices to make a rational decision. Reaching a decision can be a difficult process at the best of times, but this one is doubly so because of conflicting messages we receive both about the nature of menopause and about the value of hormone therapy. This controversy has potentially far-reaching consequences both for us as individual women and for society at large.

While it is important for us to feel we have choices and that the choices we make are in our best interests, how do we know when a choice is a *viable* choice? What factors complicate this particular decision for us? What makes the choice about hormone therapy less than straight-forward? For many of us, some very real, often hidden, pressures complicate this process.

If we feel any shame at all about our bodies, we are automatically vulnerable to suggestions that we do something or buy something to cover up or remove evidence of what doesn't feel acceptable. For example, the belief that we/our bodies are not okay *as we are* accounts for the magnitude of the cosmetic, fashion, diet and cosmetic-surgery industry. Similarly, many of us carry some element of shame about being in menopause and, therefore, aging—thus providing another market for products to mask the signs of these processes. *Any time we take medication in connection with an experience that has even the smallest amount of shame attached to it, we have good reason to proceed with great caution. It is then that we need to look closely at the motives of those who are telling us what we need. In particular, it is important to explore what this experience means to us and what expectations we have of the product being offered.* And when an experience such as menopause is so clearly influenced by cultural values and beliefs, we must take a close look at the role of medical world in that experience.

Our options are clouded when conflicting ideas and a lack of information characterize the issue. The dilemma faced by so many of us is reflected in this woman's comment:

"The only 'choices' I feel I have are taking estrogen and risking cancer—or not taking it and getting osteo-porosis! How am I supposed to decide between *those*?"

How much choice will we think we have when sleepless, sweat-filled nights add to the stress of our days? How much choice will we feel if we spend a day in public dripping from hot flashes? And if we or our partners feel our emotions are out of control as a result of menopause, each may feel that the relationship is threatened. In such situations, many of us can believe we are selfish or unfair not to seek treatment. Hormone therapy offers the possibility of not only easing our physical discomfort, but also of reassuring both ourselves and our partners that *something* is being done about what feels like a problem.

How straight-forward are our choices if we feel our health is at risk and our self esteem threatened? After all, the popular beliefs surrounding menopause imply that our body has a deficiency of hormones. Our usual response to a deficiency is to correct it—so extra hormones would appear to be a wise choice. Complicating the issue is that many of us enter menopause with a history of accepting medical authority. Combined with this is the tendency in our society to highly value science, which medicine is felt to be, and to see most problems as originating from within ourselves. This is quite opposite to the idea that our minds, bodies and health are also influenced by the beliefs, policies, values and perspectives we have absorbed and accepted from our social-cultural environment.

How much choice can we believe we have when we are afraid of aging, of disease or of losing our partner's interest? Here are some common images that can propel many of us toward hormone therapy:

 – a stooped, skeletal women, suffering osteoporosis which extra hormones might have prevented;

- a women dead because of a heart attack which extra hormones might have prevented;
- a woman alone because she has lost her "femininity," beauty, sexual attractiveness and desirability, which (the advertisments imply) pharmaceuticals could have prevented by keeping her looking younger, and, therefore, valuable;
- a poverty-stricken woman, poor because she is old and alone.

However, researchers continue to disagree about the safety of hormone therapy.

Many of us may find that hormone therapy improves the quality of our lives. It may give us a greater sense of control over our bodies, overcoming the notion that, because we are women, we are meant to passively suffer. This could be interpreted as a liberation for us, but it is hardly the basis of an *informed free choice* in a majority culture which has a long history of devaluing menstruation and menopause.

Susanne Arms, in *Immaculate Deception: A New Look at Women and Childbirth in America*, describes a woman's situation during childbirth as that one moment when she might turn, nauseous and exhausted, with a look of shock and disbelief, to the person attending her, the figure of authority. Arms describes her desperate look as one that any woman who has ever witnessed a delivery would recognize. She suggests that in a more primitive time, an attending midwife would have correctly interpreted that look to be a plea for reassurance and support. She goes on to say that today, in our culture, more likely an attending obstetrician would interpret that look as a call to stop the pain, or to take over the process for her.[129]

A case can be made that a similar situation—albeit less dramatic—exists with menopause. Like giving birth, menopause can also be a time when we can feel out of control and at the mercy of biology, fate or chance. "I don't understand what's happening to me!" or "Tell me what I can do!" can easily be heard as "Do something!" As with childbirth, unless our doctors, our families and we, ourselves, look beneath the surface of these experiences that are uniquely female, there is a strong risk that some of our cries for help will be misinterpreted as "Stop it," "Intervene" or "Do it for me" when all we really mean is "Support me as I go through it."

For many of us, there is a missing element in the search for an informed decision and it is crucial: What does menopause mean to us? To other women? How might the meanings affect our total experience of menopause? What has menopause meant to women who have already gone through it? In what ways do the physical, emotional, cultural and developmental sides of menopause interact? How does this interaction show up in our bodies and our emotions? "Is what I'm experiencing normal?" Too often these questions are ignored and our own knowledge and opinions silenced in the face of the experts to whom we have turned for answers.

I believe an informed decision about whether to take extra hormones must include three aspects: considering what personal meaning menopause has for each of us; what menopause means in our culture; and how the interaction of the many sides of our menopause affects us physically, emotionally and developmentally.

PART 3

Women in and past menopause are our society's greatest untapped natural resource. And the land in and beyond menopause is unchartered territory waiting for us to shape it in a way that pleases us. This is a challenge which takes courage and is most likely to succeed in the company of other women.

20
Exploring
Your
Menopause

Introduction to the Exercises

Many of us do not realize how much we have in common with other women, often believing that other women don't feel the way we do. As a result, we can become isolated, not only from other women, but also from parts of ourselves. This can leave us vulnerable to thinking that we, alone, feel the way we do. Or we can believe there is something uniquely wrong with us when, instead, it is something many of us share. For these reasons, I would encourage you to consider meeting with other women to do the following exercises together. You can do this with one other woman or with several. If you decide to meet in a group, the guidelines in Appendix A are designed to promote an atmosphere of trust and safety. You can also go through the exercises on your own if circumstances prevent you from meeting with other women, or if you prefer to do them by yourself. In either situation you do the exercises on your own; the difference is that the group extends your experience by providing an opportunity to share whatever part of your experience you chose.

The following are a few responses from women (most of whom were part of a group) who have completed the exercises:

"I had felt alone with the changes I've been going through. Now I know I'm definitely not alone and I'm *not* neurotic!"

"I've never felt particularly powerful before—I mean really powerful. I do now. Feels great!"

"Being in this group has meant a lot to me on a whole bunch of levels. Being past menopause, what's most exciting for me now is that I've been able to feel more in touch with a part of myself that felt very fuzzy before. Now I have a clearer sense of that part of me."

"I *like* me now! I understand what's going on in my life now, and I can tell my partner what's going on."

"I'm a different woman. I mean, I see myself a whole lot differently. And more compassionately, I might add."

"Self confidence—that's the biggest one for me."

"I know a whole lot more about myself than I did before. I'm not a mystery to myself anymore."

When we have access to each other's experiences we don't have to reinvent the wheel as we go along. We can be empowered and enriched by the perspectives and the wisdom of others. We can *build* on our experiences as women, and increase both our individual and collective energies. As individual women and as a society we are in urgent need of a solid storehouse of knowledge about menopause. A powerful way to accomplish this is for us to discuss our personal experiences of this transition with each other. As Rita Freedman notes, "a chorus of voices can transform a private pain into a public issue. Things do change when women begin to tell it like it is, the way they see and feel it."[130]

Some of the exercises involve a certain amount of reflection—that is, either taking the time to remember past events or contemplating how you feel now. Perhaps one of the most practical advantages of meeting with other women in a group is that you *guarantee* yourself the opportunity to do this reflecting. New associations and understandings can emerge from completing the exercises and discussing them with other women.

As a society, we don't often support each other in taking time for such reflection. It can, however, be a valuable process, especially during the menopause years. It can relieve stress when you allow yourself space in which to clarify your thoughts and your priorities.

On your own, with a friend, or with a group, there are no right or wrong ways to explore your menopause.

In general, as women, our experiences with our bodies/ourselves are stories not yet put to words because we are still formulating what we have to say. We have to begin first by *noticing* our experiences: the themes of our *female* lives, about us as women, and how these themes show up in our emotions/our bodies. *Naming* comes next: just what is this feeling? What name can we give it? How can we share it with others? In this way, we can *understand and make sense of our woman-experiences, including menopause. The exercises in this chapter are designed to help in this process.*

You will gain the most benefit from these exercises if you set aside the ways you think you *should* act, think or believe. Focus instead on what you *actually* feel: what do your own mind, body, emotions, memory and history tell you?

About emotions

Some of the exercises ask you about your emotions. There are no right, wrong, good or bad emotions. They just are. Looking below the surface of your menopause can sometimes reveal unexpected feelings. Expressing them where and when you feel comfortable can often help to move through them. For example, it is not uncommon to believe that if we start to cry we will never stop, but while the *fear* is real, no one dies from crying.

Sometimes we can feel "generated" anger. This is anger many of us have felt when we become aware of the extent to which we are influenced and harmed by cultural attitudes unkind to women. Anne Wilson Schaef, in her book, *Women's Reality*, makes some observations on this anger which may ease fears you may have about your anger or the anger of other women. She has observed that when we allow ourselves full, safe exploration and expression of our anger, we often learn not to fear it. As women, we may go through a phase of free-floating rage at men or the world in general which may feel empowering to us, but may be a source of concern to others. However, Schaef notes that in recognizing our anger we can become freer to get to know ourselves and other women. Schaef notes that this often results in experiencing enough self-esteem to begin to explore the ways in which we buy into the system and the ways in which we devalue ourselves. We can free ourselves to focus on broader humanistic issues that include men as well as women. We can begin to articulate a system kinder to women, men and children.[131]

About trusting our perceptions

Schaef also outlines "stoppers" that can keep us from trusting our own perceptions or wisdom. I have paraphrased these and added my own comments because I believe they have particular relevance to women discussing menopause.

1. Some of us may chose to remain silent about what we're thinking if we've received negative responses when we have spoken out. "You are really off the wall!" "How could you possibly believe that?" "You've lost your mind!" "You don't know what you're talking about!" "You must be at that time of month again!" "You must be in menopause!", are all statements that can keep the best of us quiet about what we are thinking and feeling. And they can contribute to making it difficult to trust our own perceptions and ourselves.

2. Guilt. Since most of us have been taught that our primary role in life as women is to care for others, we can easily feel guilty spending time on or with ourselves. Too often we can feel selfish rather than healthy when we spend time on ourselves. Over the years of working with women, I've often noticed that whenever women start discussing issues that are important to them, someone in the group will inevitably say, "But what about men? They have a hard time too." Or, "what about male menopause?" The assumption is somehow implicit that if we are concerned about women we are not concerned about men. In my experience, we are, as women, often more concerned about the welfare of men and children than we are about our own.

Another stopper runs something like: "There are a lot more important problems relating to women than menopause. What about day-care, health care, poverty, etc.?" The implication here is that there is a hierarchy of suffering. It's as though women have no right to focus on their concerns as long as there are other people who need help. Yet there will always be others who need help.

3. Another stopper is feeling we are an "aggressive female" or a "castrating bitch." Understandably, many of us will go to great lengths to avoid these labels, including not wanting to be associated with other women so labelled. These fears are real, yet they serve to cloud what we have in common as women. And often fear of our own anger can be involved here.

4. "You're so serious these days!" "Lighten up!" "What's happened to your sense of humor?" To seriously discuss issues affecting us does not mean we've lost our ability to laugh. There are times for both.

5. Other stoppers occur when we feel we are going to be abandoned, or when we are being patronized, ignored, or isolated.

Some of the exercises ask you to answer questions for which you may not have specific memories. What is significant here is what you believe or what you *think* was the case. If, after reflecting on a question for while, nothing comes to mind, move on to the next one. Many of the questions are phrased in several different ways to help spark your memory. One advantage to being in a group is that your memory often returns when you hear the comments of others.

Notes accompany many of the exercises. Reading them before you do the exercise could expand and deepen your understanding.

EXERCISE 1

EXPLORING YOUR INHERITANCE

Take a few moments to think about each of these questions. This will give you a sense of some of the ideas and assumptions about menopause/midlife you inherited from your family and friends.

What do you know—or not know—about your mother's menopause, your grandmother's, aunt's, older sister's, etc.? Are there family stories or anecdotes about menopause or middle-aged women in your family? Who is the first person you knew to be in menopause? What messages did you get about menopause from this person?

EXERCISE 2

SOME ORIGINS OF YOUR FEELINGS ABOUT YOUR FEMALE BODY/SELF

At the ages indicated in the following questions, focus on what you think or believe you or someone else would have said or thought at the time. Whether anyone actually said it does not matter.

Write out your responses to the following:

1. At age 13, what would your mother have said about you and/or your body if she were telling a friend about you? What would your father have said?

What would *you* have said about your body?

"At age 13, what I liked about my body was

_____ .

"At age 13, what I disliked about my body was

_____ .

2. What comments do you recall or imagine your father making about your mother's body?

3. What childhood illness or accidents have you had? How did you feel at the time? How did your mother respond to your illness? Your father? Your siblings?

4. When did you first feel concern about how your body looked? If you have *never* been worried about how others saw your body, when did you first feel pride in your body?

5. How do you feel about your body now? What would you imagine your best friend would say about your body?

6. What would you imagine your partner would say about your body?

EXERCISE 3

EXPLORING THE BEGINNINGS OF WHAT IS ENDING: MENSTRUATION

How you felt when you started menstruating will have some influence—varying from woman to woman —on how you end menstruation. Understanding your attitudes toward menstruation will help you understand your menopause. In each section, a number of questions are posed to help stimulate your memory.

1. Who first told you about menstruation (mother, father, sister, aunt, friend)?

2. How and where were you told? How did you feel? What did you pick up about menstruating from the attitudes or feelings of the person telling you? Did they talk to you before you started menstruating, or not until after?

3. What emotions did you feel when you actually started? What thoughts did you have? Who knew? Who was told? Who was not told? What did your mother say to you when you started? Your father?

4. What do you think beginning to menstruate meant in your family?

5. In what ways did your relationship with your mother change once you began menstruating? Your father? Your brother(s)? Your sister(s)? Your girl friend(s)? Boys?

Over the years, I have found that women's responses to these questions seem to fall on a continuum: some women recalled that to some extent their mothers seemed to move further away from them; and others felt their mothers seemed closer. Some possible explanations are that some mothers perceive a daughter to be a threat or a rival because the daughter is becoming a woman; other mothers feel closer because now she and her daughter share a common experience: menstruation. Most of our experiences probably lie somewhere between these two extremes.

6. Where were menstrual supplies kept in your house? Were they treated in the same way as Kleenex, for example? Were they in view? If not, did it feel as though they were put away, or were they hidden? If so, from whom?

7. Where were the used supplies put? Were they treated in any special way? Why? Did it matter who saw them?

8. What messages did you receive about cleanliness, modesty or odor during menstruation? This will have had an influence on you. What was that influence?

9. Who would you talk to about menstruating? To whom would you go if you had a problem?

10. In what way did your life change after you began menstruating? Attitudes toward your body? Restrictions—real or imagined—about the kinds of activities you took part in while menstruating? Concerns about "accidents"? Other fears?

11. If you are still menstruating, how does your partner feel about you/your body while you are menstruating? Have you ever talked or asked about these feelings?

EXERCISE 4

HOT FLASHES REVISITED

If you have either hot flashes or night sweats, it can be helpful to chart them. While this is best done throughout the day over a period of time, take a few moments now to reflect on what you have noticed about them.

1. When do they occur? In what situations or at what times? How were you feeling just before? What did you eat or drink before?

2. What emotion do you feel during each?

3. Do hot flashes or night sweats have an influence on how you feel about your femininity, sexuality or womanliness?

4. If you have night sweats and sleep with someone, how do you think that person feels about your night sweats? Accepting? Resentful? Mystified? Impatient?

By exploring these questions you will get to know your body/yourself better and give yourself more of a sense of control and understanding. Consider keeping a notebook with you so that when you have a hot flash you can answer questions such as: When? Where? What emotion was I feeling just prior to the hot flash? What was I thinking about at the time? Was I in a tense or stressful situation? What did I have to drink or eat in the hour before?

EXERCISE 5

EXPLORING SOCIETY'S INFLUENCE ON HOW YOU SEE YOURSELF/YOUR BODY

Consider watching the film/video, *Still Killing Us Softly* —about images of women in advertising—in conjunction with this exercise. It is a fascinating and entertaining lecture given by Jean Kilbourne at Harvard University, which can forever change how you look at advertising directed at women. It may be available from your local public or film library. (See Appendix B.)

Many advertisements directed at us address our critical, self-observant eye, of us observing ourselves. Diane Barthel, who analyzes gender and advertising in her book, *Putting On Appearances,* writes that appearances can sometimes take the place of self. She comments, "It is no wonder, then, that the mirror is the symbol of femininity. It is not vanity; it is necessity. It reflects the commandment that women see themselves as others see them; it is the means by which they can be at once both self (critic) and other (object)."[132] So much faith can be placed in the power of a change in appearance to "make us over" that we can neglect what is going on inside of us.

A note for groups: Once you have completed this exercise on your own and have heard the other women discuss their responses, note how you feel about your body when you hear other women talk about their bodies in negative terms? In positive terms? As a group, you may want to discuss the majority culture's standards of beauty.

Try to answer the following "off the top of your head" without analyzing your feelings.

1. Write a sentence or two about how you *feel* (versus how you think you "should" or would like to feel) about the following:
   - your breasts
   - your thighs
   - your hips
   - your vagina.

2. Do the same for how you believe your partner or lover feels about each of the above. Consider checking out the accuracy of your perceptions.

3. The part of my body I like the most is _____ .
Because _____ .

4. The part of my body I dislike the most is

_____ .

Because _____ .

5. In your daily life, what do you *do* to your body
to either change or cover up parts of it so that you/your
body will meet current popular standards of beauty
(as separate from those of general health)?

6. Are the parts of your body that you like the ones
which meet or are close to these standards?

7. Who in your life today—or in the past—thinks your
body is just fine the way it is?

8. Who in your life today—or in the past—thinks your
body should be different or changed in some way?

EXERCISE 6

YOUR BODY AS MESSENGER AND ADVISOR

Bodies as resources

Your body is an important part of your self and it
is a messenger telling you something about how you
are feeling about your life and what is important to
you. What's not working in your life is no doubt showing
up in some way in your body.

We must listen carefully to our bodies and to heed
its messages. We need to allow our body to serve as
a resource rather than a scapegoat. Our bodies are

programmed to speak authentically for themselves.[133] Unless we respect our bodies/ourselves, we are vulnerable to thinking of our bodies as our enemies. As Elissa Melamed has noted, a body which is despised and disowned may eventually take its revenge.[134] We can run away from many unpleasant experiences, but how can we run from our own bodies? They are doing the running.[135] Too often, too many of us see our bodies as obstacles to overcome rather than as allies—pitting mind against body and making it difficult to respect, listen to and fully enjoy our bodies/ourselves.

Your body is influenced by the physical, emotional, socio-cultural, economic and spiritual environment in which you live. If you haven't had a chance to do so yet, this may be the time to consider how your body is influenced by your emotions and by external factors.

How much do we ingest medicine to increase our adaption to the external world—instead of changing what we are able to change in the external to harmonize it with the internal? And what is the cumulative effect on our bodies of the meanings we and society attach to menopause? It is difficult to believe there is no effect.

There seems to be an underlying assumption some of us have that, in order to be "liberated," we must keep separate from our bodies. For example, it is common for many of us to believe that we should strive to overcome all evidence of menstruation and menopause—this is, to ignore both as much as possible, or to try to ensure that they have as little influence on our lives as possible. Yet this is not liberation: we are our bodies. Somehow, we must find ways to structure of our lives to accommodate the cycles of our bodies— rather than attempt to mold our bodies to systems of time and work that have never taken these cycles into account. Otherwise, we risk losing touch with our bodies, and, therefore, ourselves. And, in the process, we leave ourselves vulnerable to exploitation and to having needs *created for us* rather than meeting our own.

Sometimes healing the discomforts of our bodies means paying attention to our deepest fears. In our majority culture there is a popular belief that says that if we have a discomfort in our bodies our options are limited to being in pain or *taking* something to relieve it. However, it may be that we have to do something about a situation instead.

Elissa Melamed writes:

- Our bodies are records of our lives as we have lived them up to now. They can change as our lives change, and respond to change in our beliefs and attitudes.

- Our feelings about ourselves affect our posture, breathing, and muscle tone. Even our hormone levels have been shown to be responsive to our thoughts. For example, if we think we are "over the hill," we may be inhibiting the production of the female hormones estrogen and progesterone. Our beliefs about aging can affect our very cells.

- We don't know what aging in women would look like in a society that was supportive of it.

- We cannot be truly ourselves if we deny the flow of time.

A word about the words "psychosomatic" and "hypochondriac"—terms so often used to negatively label women: The implication is that a person so labelled would have a more valid concern if it were one of a "purely" physical nature. Each of these terms is silently accompanied by the label "neurotic." As with so many labels, once it has been used we tend to lose sight of the person. This person may be a woman whose body is telling her, and us, that something is not well with her life. We need to recognize that illness remains one of the few *acceptable* ways for us to voice female complaints and to get our needs for attention, "space" and nurturing met.

1. Close your eyes and focus on your breathing for a while. Notice the areas of tension in your body. Where does stress show up in your body? What seems to trigger it?

2. If stress affects one place in your body more than another, choose the most noticeable one for this exercise. Close your eyes, take some deep breaths and relax. With your eyes still closed, focus in on the part which feels stress the most. For me, it's my shoulders. For others it may be their stomach, jaw, neck, etc. Now imagine that you are giving that part of your body a voice. Pretend that it can talk. What would it say if you ask it how it feels? For example, my shoulders have been known to say, "We are Lafern's shoulders and we're exhausted because it feels like we're carrying too much weight. So relax!."

3. Now ask the same part what will happen to it if this level of stress continues. For example, my shoulders have informed me that this level of tension also affects my neck, jaw, head and back.

EXERCISE 7

EXPLORING THE RELATIONSHIP BETWEEN YOUR EMOTIONS AND YOUR BODY

1. Close your eyes and recall a very happy moment in your life. Focus on it: try to see it in your mind's eye. Immerse yourself in it. How does your body feel while you are thinking happy thoughts? Now notice where happiness shows up in your body. For example, mine show up most in my chest and throat.

2. Recall a moment or event in your life that caused you to feel extremely sad or unhappy. For a moment, immerse yourself in this memory. Now notice where sadness shows up in your body.

3. Do the same for a time when you felt intense anger or rage. Where do you feel anger in your body?

4. Do you smile or laugh to cover up nervousness, sadness or anger? Consider the extent to which this gives others mixed messages and how this may affect your relationships with others.

EXERCISE 8

CHANGING HOW YOU SEE YOUR BODY/YOURSELF

If you don't already love your body, growing to love it/yourself requires that you become familiar with and accept it/you. In the face of all the other messages that you are receiving from that wide world out there, perhaps mostly from the media, try to see and feel your body in a different light. The purpose of this exercise is to explore acceptance of your body, as is, beyond basic health considerations. Here are some suggestions which have helped other women begin to accept their changing bodies:

1. Close your eyes. Imagine that you are standing naked in front of a full length mirror. Relax. Simply notice how your body looks without doing anything such as pulling in your stomach, etc. Notice your thoughts and feelings as you look. Are you judging your body? If so, how do you *feel* as you judge yourself?

2. Repeat this exercise but this time actually stand naked in front of a mirror and see if your responses are the same. Are they mostly positive or mostly negative? If your thoughts are mostly negative, find more positives—they *are* there.

3. Of the people closest to you, who would agree with your assessment of your body? Who would disagree or say you are being too hard on yourself?

4. Has one part of your body/yourself suffered more than another—either through pain, injury, chronic illness or harsh judgements from others or yourself? Locate one square inch on this part. For the next few days or a week, plan to give that small place a great deal of positive attention such as a massage, special oils, write a poem about it, decorate it. After a few days or a week, do another area. Spend a few days or more on this spot. Keep going until you have covered the entire area. Then move on to any other parts you have had difficulty with.

5. Write a note of thanks to yourself/your body for serving you so well throughout the years.

6. In what ways do you restrict your body's movement in the clothes, shoes or accessories you wear? How do you bind, squeeze, push, pull or strain your body by either what you wear or how you wear it? For example, a shoulder bag hanging from one shoulder will keep that shoulder raised and can easily result in neck and back tension. How can you change these practices so as to be kinder to your body/yourself?

7. If this has been difficult for you, consider checking out either a book or a course on accepting your body. For example, the book, *Transforming Body Image* by Marcia Hutchinson has some excellent exercises to help in this process.

For those who can afford it, having a weekly massage can go a long way toward helping you begin to appreciate your body. If your first thought is that this is an extravagance, think about how much you spend on your car, or on products to hide what you don't love about your body. You could trade massages with a good friend. If you've spent the better part of your life disliking even one small part of your body, menopause may be a time for change. When we like our bodies we free up blocked energy and so open up further possibilities for ourselves.

EXERCISE 9

YOUR RELATIONSHIP WITH YOUR PHYSCIAN

A physician is trained long and extensively in a particular way of viewing the human body and of treating illness. When you go to a physician it is important to understand what that view is, and to determine if it is one you are comfortable with. There are many good reasons why I visit my physician. However, I understand that there is much that can influence my health for which she may have little or no training. Nor do I expect her to. For example, what I put into my body will naturally influence my body/my self. Yet most physicians don't have training in nutrition, food additives or chemicals, or knowledge of, or interest in, non-medical alternatives for curing what ails us.

At issue is not individual physicians or even the medical community at large, but the position of privilege and power which most of us have allowed our physicians. The problem is the emphasis and the proportion of authority and expertise we give to the medical community. When we hand over our personal authority and power, we further separate from the wisdom and knowledge which our own bodies and personal experience give us.

When you visit a physician about menopause, keep in mind that many physicians place great credibility on the information they receive about menopause from medical texts and pharmaceutical companies, much more than they do the information from women themselves. The information in texts and journals reflect cultural attitudes about women. For example, when drug ads in four leading medical journals were analyzed, it was found that males were more often portrayed as needing psychoactive drugs because of tension related to *their outside world*. On the other hand, women were more often said to require these drugs because of general anxiety or depression. That is, in the case of a woman, the cause of the problem is most often seen as being *within her*—it is *she* who needs fixing. For a man, the cause is more likely to be attributed to a source outside of him; it is something in his outer world which is the problem. The danger here is the implication that men have "real" problems while women have "neurotic" problems. The researchers concluded that these ads may encourage physicians to interpret symptoms presented by women as reflecting emotional illness, and those of men as reflecting physical illness, even though the actual symptom may be identical.[136]

Some things that help: see your physician as a resource, rather than as someone with an authority greater than your own or that of other women; get a second opinion when you are unsure; take a buddy (an advocate) with you if you are *even the slightest bit* uncomfortable or confused when you see your physician; ask for a longer appointment when you know you have a lot of questions to ask. No expert has all the answers and, most important, you are your own best expert on your body.

1. Are you comfortable with how your physician speaks to you? Do you feel listened to in the fullest sense of the word? Do you feel like an equal consulting an equal? Or do you feel inferior in any way? Do you feel respected for your inner knowledge of your own body?

2.   Do you feel your physician is aware of the impact of cultural beliefs and values on women at midlife?

3. If you are not completely happy with your physician, do you feel at ease about switching to someone else?

EXERCISE 10

YOUR MENOPAUSE AS A TRANSITON IN YOUR LIFE

Recall that menopause is a transition and, as such, it may be influenced by how you have gone through other major transitions. Menopause and adolescence both involve physical changes which affect our sense of identity as females. In adolescence you were moving away from childhood and into young adulthood. That process lead to an identity shift and to changes in how you saw and felt about yourself. In adolescence you may have felt that anything "childish" had to be set aside, if not scorned. Although you may have imagined it as exciting, the adulthood that lay ahead was also an unknown. In the meantime, being a teenager meant being in a time of transition between childhood and adulthood. Many of us find similarities between how we felt during our teenage years and how we feel during menopause. This doesn't mean reverting to adolescence. Rather, it is a reminder that both these times are transitions that involve hormonal changes with considerable social-cultural significance.

1. In adolescence, what did you miss the most about leaving childhood?

2. What was most difficult for you during your adolescence? (Relationships? Your body? Sexual identity? Family? School? How you felt about yourself? The future?)

3. Now that you are in (or approaching) menopause, what will you miss the most about being a young(ish) woman?

4. What do you see yourself moving away from with menopause? Toward?

5. All change can feel threatening on some level. In what ways does being in menopause feel like a threat to you? (Health? Body? Relationships? Family? Work? The future?) How do you notice this in your daily life or relationships?

EXERCISE 11

EXPLORING YOUR FEELINGS OF FEMININITY

We get most of our first ideas about women's and men's roles and values from our parents (who in turn got it from their parents and from the culture in which they grew up).

1. How do you think your mother felt about being a woman? If she had to complete these sentences to sum up her feelings in a word or two, what would she say? What's important here is *what you believe she would say.*

A woman (or a woman's life) is _____ .

Women are valuable because/for _____ .

Women are good for _____ .

2. What is your perception of how your father felt about women in general? If he had to complete these sentences in a few words, what do you think he would say?

Women are _____ .

Women have value because _____ .

Women are good for _____.

3. Setting aside "shoulds," wishes and ideals, how would you answer the same questions? How are they the same and different from those of your parents?

4. What do think of as your most feminine traits, characteristics, habits or ideas? What do you feel is most feminine about you?

5. When do you feel the most feminine? What most often brings out the feminine in you? Why?

6. Both men and women have masculine and feminine qualities. What do you feel are your more masculine traits, characteristics, habits or ideas?

7. When do you feel the most masculine? Why?

EXERCISE 12

EXPLORING YOUR HISTORY OF FERTILITY AND INFERTILITY

Our memories are stored in our bodies as well as our minds. For example, a certain touch or smell—or a physical change such as menopause—can trigger thoughts or memories of experiences long past.

About "unfinished business"

When old secrets, fears and sorrows are not identified, brought out into the open and allowed their emotions they can retain the power to influence our present-day behavior without our awareness. The older, more painful and secretive the experience is, the bigger and more frightening the surrounding emotion can be. A vicious cycle may then be set in motion: a fear that if the memories are brought to the surface a mountain of emotion will overcome us and our loved ones; that opening the "can of worms" will only cause more difficulty for everyone; that the crying will never stop; that the anger will seriously harm others. And so the feelings are often buried, and so they retain their power. One way past deep emotion is to go through it, and one way to loosen the grip of fear is to name its source. When old wounds, secrets and fears are named, aired and allowed to heal in the light of present day, deep change follows.

For some of us, menopause, like some other life experiences, can trigger unhappy memories from child-hood such as those of sexual, emotional or physical abuse. Even for the bravest of us, this can be frightening. If this has happened to you, I urge you to find a therapist trained in this kind of work. Someone whose judgment you trust, or a local social-service agency can help you find one.

* * * * * * * * * *

For most of us, menopause ends our time of fertility, either actually or symbolically. This makes it a natural time to reflect on your history of fertility or nonfertility. Recall that the way we move through a transition is influenced by the extent to which we recognize what we are leaving behind. This can free us up to better see the potential in what we are moving toward.

1. Have you ever tried to become pregnant and been unable to? How did this affect you emotionally and physically? What procedures did you go through to try to become pregnant? Did you decide to be childless even though you were fertile?

How have these experiences influenced your feelings about yourself as a woman? How was your relationship with your partner affected?

2. If you have never had a child, for whatever reason, what does being in menopause mean to you? Is this more a time of relief? Grief? Or both?

3. Have you been pregnant? How many times? At what ages? Were they planned or not? How did you feel when you first realized you were pregnant? Did your emotions change as you moved through the pregnancy? Did you feel well supported and understood? Or did you feel essentially alone in the experience? How did being pregnant influence your feelings about yourself as a woman? What were the implications for your health: emotionally, physically and spiritually? What are your feelings, today, about the experience? What, if anything, would you have done differently?

4. Have you had an abortion? How many? At what ages? What were the circumstances? What were your emotions? How did having an abortion influence your feelings about yourself as a woman? Did you feel supported or basically alone? What were the implica-

tions for your health: emotionally, physically and spiritually? What are your feelings, today, about the experience? What, if anything, would you have done differently?

5. If you have been in labor, what was it like for you? Recall how your body responded. What were the physical surroundings? Were you comfortable? What was the range of your emotions from beginning to end? Did you feel well supported or more alone? What were your feelings about being a woman at that time? What are your feelings, today, about the experience? What, if anything, would you have done differently?

6. If you have given birth, what was it like for you? How did it feel physically? Emotionally? Spiritually? What were the implications on your health? After giving birth, how did you feel about yourself as a woman? How has that event influenced your life?

7. If you have experienced a stillbirth or miscarriage, what was that experience like for you? Did you feel supported or alone? How did it influence your feelings about yourself as a woman? What influence did that experience have on your life? On your relationship with your partner? What, if anything, would you have done differently?

8. Reflect on whether or not you have any unresolved feelings about any of these experiences. If you do—or if you are uncertain about whether you do or not—you may want to consider writing a note to the source of the emotion, telling about what it was like for you. This could be a note to an unborn child, your body,

partner, family, physician, nurses, friends or to yourself at that age. The intent is not to give this writing to anyone, although you may decide to do this, but to acknowledge what happened and to grieve it if necessary so that you can let it go. This experience can play a powerful role in resolving grief.

EXERCISE 13

EXPLORING YOUR FEELINGS ABOUT YOUR SEXUALITY AND SENSUALITY

One of the major "stoppers" many of us feel about expressing our sexuality is the notion that a woman who "looks her age" should keep her sensuality hidden. She might be able to get away with it if she has a man visible—because expressions of sensuality in an older women are too often viewed as inappropriate unless she is with someone else.

An older man with a younger woman is a common sight. Yet, the few of us who enjoy a young lover must first break a taboo. Often our mate risks ridicule either as a fortune hunter if we are financially secure, or as a neurotic hung up on a mother figure.[137] Too often, the implication is that these are the only reasons why a younger man would want to be with a woman who is "over the hill."

Nelson W. Aldrich, Jr., in his article in *Lear's* magazine, suggests that far more European women feel fundamentally at home in their bodies than do most North American women. He attributes this in part to the "brutal singularity" of the American image of beauty. The mass media shapes this image because it is dedicated to attracting and holding as many consumers as possible. The result is "a young Christie Brinkley in a perfect bathing suit on a perfect beach."[138] Consequently, the American erotic-aesthetic imagination is shaped and saturated by Brinkleys in swimsuits. And, thus, forms of beauty and sensuality not tied to youth are rendered largely invisible. Aldrich writes:

"The rule of youth is the single most soul-destroying, pleasure-denying, love-shrivelling consequence of living under the domination of American beauty. It blinds us to the loveliness, the libidinous loveliness, of the fully lived life. A people who do not see the sexual allure of Jeanne Moreau's love-spent face, who do not respond to the magnificent ripeness of Sophia Loren, who cannot hear the erotic agony in the voice of Maria Callas—such a people deserve their subservience to the image of Christie Brinkley. And we are punished for it. Our insistence of youth, health and sportswear confirms in us a kind of willful innocence, a refusal of commitment and responsibility, as though the only desirable state of mind and body in this country were not experience, not actuality, not consequence, but a permanent condition of [attempts to retain youth].[139]

Aldrich also suggests that a contributing factor in what he sees as the European/North American difference lies in the fact that in Europe children are with their families longer, allowing for plenty of time and occasion for girls to become familiar with the ways of men with women, and women with men. In North America this function is often haphazardly and perhaps shallowly performed by a cross between the television and the peer group.

Aldrich also notes that many North American parents

seem convinced that the future belongs to the young, which translates in the family that grown-ups have nothing to teach their children that the experts and the up-to-date can't teach them a lot better.

A note for groups: You may want to discuss Nelson Aldrich's comments.

Setting aside "shoulds" or ideals, try to answer the following "off the top of your head":

1. How old does a woman have to be before sensual flirting in public will feel unacceptable to most of the people you know?

2. Who do you know personally, who is considered to be both old and sensual?

EXERCISE 14

EXPLORING YOUR NEEDS

1. These days, what basic emotional, physical or spiritual needs do you have? Set aside any thoughts you may have about being "needy." It is natural and normal to have needs. Priorize those needs.

2. Setting aside any thoughts you may have about being selfish, in what practical ways can you go about getting those needs met? If this feels impossible or difficult, plan to talk about it with another person whom you trust to be objective.

3. In what ways can you pay special and positive attention to yourself/your body and the changes of menopause? In particular, how can you do this from a perspective of health rather than sickness?

For many of us, the only acceptable way to meet our needs for rest, attention or time alone is through illness. It can be difficult to give ourselves permission to pay attention to our own needs simply because we have them. If this is true for you, consider making time for yourself without having to be "under the weather" to do it.

4. Do your family and friends know what your needs are? If not, consider telling them, even if you have to add in a firm voice that this is not being neurotic or "needy." Let them know that you are leaving a stage of your life—one that may well have been centered around care-giving—and that they may notice some changes in you in this area.

5. Who and what nurtures/empowers/energizes/excites you? Who and what drains you? To the extent that you can, use this information in your decisions about how you spend your time.

EXERCISE 15

EXPLORING WAYS OF THINKING ABOUT MENOPAUSE

"When sleeping beauty wakes up, she's almost 50 years old."

– *Maxine Cumin*[140]

Years down the road, what we currently call "decline" may be viewed in a completely different way. What is happening in your compost pile—decay or development? It depends on your perspective. Is the end of our physical life the end of our existence? There are many different views on these topics, most of which are affected by the culture which has the most influence on us. What are your views? Are they the ones you inherited from your parents? Do they fit with the rest of your current beliefs or experiences?

In other cultures, and at other times in history, menopause was considered a period of adjustment, a time when a woman's body sought to balance and adjust itself to a new, non-fertile role. Mind and body were not separate, with identity, self-hood, and consciousness residing in the body as well as the mind. Thus, a woman at menopause would be going through the process of seeking the balance and adjustment necessary for her upcoming new roles. Women, along with all other living creatures, were participants in nature, and, as such, experienced seasons in their lives.

As we recognize the attitudes and values associated with menopause, we urgently need new ways of thinking and talking about it. How you think and talk about your menopause can influence your physical and emotional experience of it.

1. How do you refer to your menopause? Do you own it, make it your own? Is it an "it" or is it a "my"? An enemy or a companion?

2. What can you add to this list of alternate definitions of menopause:
   - From the 1930s: "The time for women to review their daily lives and consider whether they should alter them in any way."[141]
   - From the author Margaret Atwood: a pause during which to reconsider men.[142]
   - From Emily Martin, author of *The Woman In The*

Body, as the "Indian summer" of a woman's life, a period of increased vigor, optimism, and even of physical beauty.[143]

3. In what ways can you change how you think about your menopause, aging, hot flashes, night sweats, etc.? For example, some women refer to their hot flashes as power surges.

EXERCISE 16

UNEARTHING "INVISIBLE" VALUES

The majority culture tends to convey to both women and men that in order to be truly fulfilled we must have a child. This implies we need to be fertile to be whole. Wholeness can then be seen to depend on fertility. These beliefs contribute to negative attitudes toward menopause.

If we are to change popular views of menopause, we must first examine our own.

1. In general, what is powerful and valuable about your femaleness, about who you are and what you contribute to the world *in addition to* your sexuality, child bearing or role as a mother? What perspectives, wisdom, knowledge, values, etc. do we, as women, have to offer to society?

2. How can you think or talk about yourself and other women in ways which acknowledge these character-istics or contributions?

For example, many of us tend to compliment a girl or a woman by remarking on her appearance; whereas with boys and men we tend to mention what they do. Thus, we may unconsciously reinforce value for appearance *more* in females than in males.

3. We naturally take care of that which we love. When you love your body/yourself, it is not a chore to exercise or otherwise take care of yourself. If you don't already love your body, in what ways can you begin to?

EXERCISE 17

EXPLORING OTHER WAYS OF THINKING ABOUT MENSTRUATION

Changing ideas of femininity and menopause means changing how we think about and react to menstruation. We play a role in conveying to our girl children and to others that beginning menstruation means becoming a woman, and that part of becoming a "capital W Woman" means being able to bear children. This contributes to linking femininity, value and womanliness to child bearing. As we have seen, this is very much a problem not only for women past menopause, but for women who do not have children, for whatever reason. When we tell our children—male and female— about being women, how often do we include the fact of menopause and what is unique to women *in addition* to being able to bear a child?

On women, cycles and time

Dena Taylor, author of the book, *Red Flower: Rethinking Menstruation*, suggests that "menstruation is a time for sleeping and dreaming, meditation, yoga, and dancing. A time for healing, being creative, figuring things out. A dark and inward time, a sensual time, a powerful time."[144] While a busy life schedule may not allow for all of this, if you are still menstruating, try doing something along this line on the day before or on the first day of your periods.

Menstruation connects us to nature, to the larger cycles of birth and death and to the relationship between endings and beginnings—and suggests a cyclical, rather than the usual linear version of time. Emily Martin writes that all women in our society share the experience of housekeeping their own bodies—bodies whose fluids, demands and changes rarely fit with any form of organized time in our industrialized society.[145]

Despite the central position of menstruation in our lives as females, it does not play a role in the time frames of the working world. Instead, there is the assumption and expectation that we will adjust our bodies and cycles to fit the time frames of society. As Elissa Melamed writes:

"The grim continuity of work life—with its eight-hour days and forty-hour weeks ad infinitum—makes the 'messy,' unpredictable female body seem deviant. We too share this male norm and try to approximate it. We apologize for our bodies. But this is not everywhere the case. Most nonindustrial cultures recognize female periodicity and accommodate to it. What if we too could experience our discontinuities of menstruation, pregnancy, and menopause not as inconveniences to be minimized, but as opportunities to reestablish our connection with nature?"[146]

If both women and men menstruated, we would most likely alter our activities, as Emily Martin suggests, to "maximize the special powers released around the time of menstruation while minimizing the discomforts."[147] By extension, this new way of thinking about menstruation would influence how we think about menopause.

1. If you are still menstruating, consider how you respond your periods. What is your attitude toward your menstruation?

2. In what small ways can you change your life so as to notice and accommodate how you feel during menstruation? In particular, how can you do this as an honoring or celebration rather than as a condition or a sickness?

3. In what way can you assist the younger women or girls in your life to re-think their attitudes toward menstruation?

EXERCISE 18

LOOKING AT THE YEARS AHEAD

Try to stay with how you actually feel versus how you think you "should" feel.

1. After menopause, as an "older woman" what will be possible that was not possible before?

2. How old is an "old" woman? Who do you think of when you think of an old woman? What do you like about her? Is there anything you dislike about her?

3. What misgivings or fears do you have about aging?

4. How do you imagine you will change physically, emotionally, spiritually?

5. What are the advantages of growing older? Being "old"? What are you looking forward to?

6. What does "acting your age" mean to you now? What could it mean?

EXERCISE 19

CELEBRATION

"It seems a pity to have a built-in rite of passage and to dodge it, to evade it, and to pretend that nothing has changed. That is to dodge and evade one's womanhood, to pretend one's like a man."

– *Ursula LeGuin*[148]

This can be a time to honor where you've been, where you are, and where you are going. And, if you are in a group, you have reason to celebrate the time you have spent together.

One of the many ways to do this is to plan a ritual, either individually or as a group. Rituals are not necessarily elaborate or rule-laden ceremonies performed by experts and undergone by followers. A ritual is whatever feels like a ceremony, a symbolic act which has meaning for you. For example, one of my rituals on returning to my home in the woods is to go to the river, breath deeply and thank Mother Nature for all this. Small and large rituals are sprinkled throughout our lives. Like our emotions, they provide color and drama, highlighting what is meaningful to us.

Some suggestions:

- Plan a ritual—or include a portion—that fits with your particular cultural background, or which in other ways has personal historical meaning for you.
- In some way, include the idea of a passage: moving away from one part of your life and moving toward another.
- There are no rules: use your imagination. Historically, rituals have qualities such as going slowly so as to absorb the moment(s) and thinking about what you are doing and what it symbolizes for you. Take a mental snapshot of the moment. Think of it as celebrating the fact that after all you've been through, you are still here, growing and changing.
- An exercise that can be very powerful is to write as though you were your own menstrual blood. Here is the beginning of one's woman's writing: "I am Laura's menstrual blood. I came to her when she was 13. Her body took a while to get used to me and she had mixed feelings about my presence in her life. I've been with her for 35 years and we have had quite a time together. In 1962 I stopped for a while when...." This process will eventually take you to your menopause.
- You are, symbolically, walking through a gate, leaving behind a way of being defined and seeing yourself as a woman, to another way, the story of which has yet to be written.
- Arrange to go away for a weekend in nature—either alone or with your group—for the sole purpose of celebrating the fact of yourselves as women approaching, in or past menopause.

* * * * * * * * * *

Appendix A

In the Company of Women: Guidelines for Groups

An overview of the group program follows so that you will have some idea of what's involved. Please remember these are suggestions only. Naturally, you may want to adapt them to suit what is most important to you.

Overview of Group Program

Purpose: to discuss and explore your experiences of menopause. The program is designed to be a series of discussions: the focus is not on therapy or problem solving.

Content of each session: Individual questions and exercises which are designed to help you explore what menopause means to you and how these meanings may influence you physically and emotionally. While with the group, you each complete each exercise on your own. Then you discuss the exercise as a group. **OR,** you may prefer to forego the exercises and discuss a chapter of this book instead.

Length, Time and Dates: This program has been designed for nine sessions of two hours each. As the group needs may vary, a different time frame may be required.

Size of group: I suggest five to ten members. This allows you to hear a variety of experiences. A group of fewer than five can have difficulties if one or more members need to be away at a given time. A group larger than 12 runs the risk of some members becoming "lost." Also, the details of arranging times, etc. are more complicated with increased size.

Membership: women in, near or past menopause.

Guidelines for Groups

There is an advantage to asking all members to read this book beforehand. In this way, you will have a common body of knowledge and an understanding of some of the cultural dynamics of menopause.

If you all know each other, you may not need these guidelines. However, they can be useful if some or all of the group members are strangers. Some of us are comfortable joining a group; others are torn between liking the idea and feeling nervous about it. Some of us have had unpleasant experiences being in a group or may feel shy or hesitant about discussing anything personal with others. Consequently, I believe it is worth taking the time to make everyone as comfortable as possible.

Locating other members

Unless you already know women interested in participating, consider posting a notice in places likely to catch women's attention. You may want to include an overview of the program and a quote or two from this book that you think would capture a woman's interest.

Or, you could contact a local community organization and ask them to help organize a group and provide a space.

Leader or No Leader?

I suggest compromising between having a leader and being a leaderless group. If you are meeting in each other's home, that week's host could be responsible for details such as beginning and ending the meeting on time. Knowing that time limits are taken care of can allow everyone to relax and enjoy themselves. There is also a lot of security in knowing you can be home when you planned to be.

Stages of a group

Groups go through stages, changing as members get comfortable with each other and with the topic. People entering a group for the first time have questions such as: Will this group be what I need? Who are these people? Can I trust them? How will I be treated here? For this reason, Exercises A, B and C can be particularly valuable. A group usually feels a greater need for a leader during the first couple of meetings, and less so as everyone becomes used to each other. The early and sometimes awkward beginning stage can be made easier by following the guidelines outlined here and having the material in this book in common.

About being in a group

Taking confidentiality seriously builds trust, as does suspending judgements—especially those regarding life style, partners, sexuality, abortions, religion, politics, etc. We have many reasons for doing what we do and making the choices we have made in our lives. Focus instead on *what you have in common as women.*

The art of communication

Listening to each other with care, interest and respect

is essential. Sitting in a close circle promotes equality and allows everyone to easily see and hear each other. If you allow time for each of you to have your say, even the reticent and shy will be heard. We each formulate our thoughts in varying ways and at different speeds. Anyone who prefers not to speak can simply ''pass.''

Try to take a few moments at the beginning of each meeting to check in with each other. In this way you let each other know ''where you're at.'' If you are worried about your partner at home with a case of the flu, it can be helpful to let the others know. Then the worried frown on your forehead is less likely to be misinterpreted as another emotion—such as boredom or disapproval. As a group you may want to agree to limit this checking-in time. At the end of each meeting, take a few moments to close off, perhaps sharing what you got out of the session.

About including a new member once the group has started

Adding a new member means you now have a new group and issues of trust and safety can come up for the old as well as the new member. If someone wants to add a new member, be sure you all agree.

* * * * * * * * * *

I suggest that you do most of the exercises while you are with the group (instead of beforehand) because hearing about the experiences of others can stimulate your memories and feelings and can greatly enrich your experience.

More than enough material has been provided for nine

weekly meetings of two hours each. As you may not be able to get through all the exercises in nine sessions, as a group you may wish to decide which are most important. My suggestion is that you read through an exercise before doing it.

At your first meeting, you may want to mention confidentiality and the other points made in the "Guidelines for Groups."

The following three exercises are designed to be used during your first and second meetings. The purpose of these exercises is to introduce yourselves and your experiences to the group in a way that will promote trust, safety and good communication.

EXERCISE A

1. Divide into groups of two (with one group of three if you have an odd number). If the space is available, you may want to move to separate corners of the room.

2. Take turns with your partner (for about five minutes each) introducing yourself and briefly saying something about yourself and what prompted you to join the group. When you return to the larger group, your *partner* will be introducing you to the larger group and saying a few words about what you have shared with her. Therefore, before you return to the larger group, ask your partner if there is anything she told you that she'd rather you not mention to the group.

3. Return to the larger group. Each person introduces her partner and briefly says a few words about her.

EXERCISE B

1. Choose a different partner and divide into groups of two again. Introduce yourselves, then take about 10 minutes each to tell each other about your menopause.

For example: Is (or was) menopause what you expected? Do you feel it is on time or not? What do you find most troublesome, difficult or pleasurable? What do you notice the most: physical or emotional changes? What concerns do you have? Note: Having an easy menopause does not equal moral superiority, nor does having a troublesome menopause mean there is something wrong with you. Freedom from menopause or health problems is not a sign of virtue.

When you have each finished, take a few moments to repeat back to your partner your understanding of what she said. You don't have to recall every detail. The idea is to be able to tell the larger group the basics of how your partner is experiencing menopause. Again, because you will be speaking for each other, check if there is anything your partner does not want mentioned to the larger group.

2. Return to the larger group. Take turns telling the group about your partner's experience of menopause.

3. As a group, you may wish to discuss what you have in common in the way of menopausal experiences.

EXERCISE C

1. Individually, write out your responses to Exercise 1: Exploring Your Inheritance. Take 10-15 minutes.

2. Break up into groups of two, with yet a different partner if possible.

3. Take turns telling each other about your responses to Exercise 1.

4. Decide if you want to speak for yourselves or each other when you return to the larger group. Share with the group some of what you discussed with your partner.

5. As a group, you may wish to discuss *what you had in common* or what stood out for you.

Format for the remaining exercises

First, complete each exercise on your own, in the group. As a group, either decide how long you want to give yourselves, or just wait until most of you are finished. *I suggest giving yourselves ample time as the idea is to allow time for reflection.* Secondly, take turns telling the group about your responses/answers, or what you learned from the exercise, or what stood out for you. Feel free to leave out what doesn't feel comfortable to share with the others. There are no right or wrongs here. Thirdly, as a group, it can be helpful to summarize your similarities and differences when you have finished sharing your responses.

* * * * * * * * * *

Appendix B

Some books and resources:

A Friend Indeed: A Newsletter for Women in the Prime of Life. P.O. Box 515, Place du Parc Station, Montreal, Quebec, H2W 2P1, OR, P.O. Box 1710, Champlain, New York, 12919-1710. Published 10 times a year, monthly except July and August, under the direction of Janine O'Leary Cobb, author of *Understanding Menopause.* Offers the latest news, views, research and items of interest to women in or near menopause. Letters from readers share their personal experiences and remedies for menopausal concerns. An excellent resource. If you have specific menopausal concerns, request a list of the back issues for valuable information.

Barthel, Diane (1988). *Putting On Appearances: Gender and Advertising.* Philadelphia: Temple University Press. Fascinating reading.

Bourne, Edmund (1990). *The Anxiety and Phobia Workbook.* Oakland, CA: New Harbinger. Good, practical information and exercises related to stress and anxiety.

Burnside, Beverly. (1990). *Depression is a Feminist Issue: A Resource Manual for the Social Health Outreach Program (SHOP)* and *Leader's Manual for the Social Health Outreach Program (SHOP): A Social Treatment for Depression.* Published by the Mature Women's Network, 2nd Floor, 411 Dunsmuir Street, Vancouver, B.C., V6B 1X4. This kit provides session-by-session guidelines for conducting a social therapy for depression (other than bipolar or "manic" depression). Intended to be used by the lay person or professional and of particular interest to women suffering from, or at risk of, depression. This program explores the ways in which social circumstances can influence depression in women.

Cobb, Janine O'Leary (1993, Revised edition). *Understanding Menopause*, Key Porter. This is the book I recommend the most for her easy-to-read coverage of the hormone debate, and the range of physical experiences and what you can do about them.

DeMarco, Carolyn (1991). *Take Charge of Your Body, A Guide to Women's Health* (Rev. Ed). The Last Laugh Inc., P.O. Box 66, Winlaw, B.C., V0G 2J0.

Freedman, Rita. (1986). *Beauty Bound*. Toronto: Heath.

Greenspan, Miriam (1983). *A New Approach to Women & Therapy*. New York: McGraw-Hill. Written for the general reader. A good introduction to the world of psychology as it relates to women, especially if you have ever considered therapy.

Hutchinson, Marcia (1985). *Transforming Body Image: Learning to Love the Body You Have*. Freedom, CA: Crossing Press.

Johnson, Karen (1991). *Trusting Ourselves: The Complete Guide to Emotional Well-Being For Women*. New York: Atlantic Monthly Press. Written for the general reader, it covers every aspect of psychology as it applies to women. Very comprehensive.

Martin, Emily (1987). *The Woman in the Body: A Cultural Analysis of Reproduction*. Boston: Beacon Press. A definitive work.

Melamed, Elissa (1983). *Mirror, Mirror: The Terror of Not Being Young*. New York: Simon & Schuster. Wonderful. Written with humor, insight and compassion.

Miller, Jean Baker (1986). *Toward a New Psychology of Women* (2nd Edition). Boston: Beacon Press. Already a classic.

Schaef, Anne Wilson (1985). *Women's Reality: An Emerging Female System in a White Male Society.* New York: Harper & Row. Easy to read, great perspectives.

Still Killing Us Softly (1987) Cambridge Documentary Films, Inc. This film can forever change how you see advertising relating to girls and women. Highly recommended. Check your local public or film library.

Notes

1 Weideger, p. 13.
2 Cobb (1993), p. 9.
3 In Cochran & Claspell.
4 Sheehy, p. 256.
5 Belenky et al, p. 146.
6 Posner (1979) and Stimpson (1982) discuss this further.
7 Melamed, p. 44.
8 Freedman, p. 206.
9 In Sontag.
10 Melamed, p. 53-54.
11 Lock, M., letter to the editor, *Healthsharing,* Spring, 1991.
12 Martin, p. 174.
13 Emily Martin also makes this point.
14 Miller, Alice, p. 173.
15 Weideger, p. 15.
16 In Cobb, 1988.
17 Weideger, p. 14.
18 Barthel, pp. 156-159.
19 Ussher, p. 29.
20 Weideger, p. 9.
21 Weideger, p. 10.
22 Weideger, p. 220-221.
23 Ussher, p. 42.
24 Ussher, pp. 30-42.
25 Weideger, p. 225.
26 Weideger, p. 10.
27 Martin, pp. 19-20.
28 Miller, Alice, p. 181.
29 For example, "mankind" is synonymous with "humankind":
As noted in earlier chapters, our language provides evidence
of our most pervasive attitudes and beliefs.
30 Rich, p. 11.
32 In Brownmiller.
33 Lakoff & Scherr, p. 181.
34 Unger, p. 244.
35 Gornick, pp.70-71.
36 Weideger, pp. 208-209.
37 Kaplan, H. (1974), p. 111, in Ussher, p. 129.
38 Freedman, p. 207.

39 Aldrich, p. 60.

40 Aldrich, p. 60.

41 Brownmiller, p. 212.

42 Lakoff & Scherr, p. 169.

43 Cobb (1988), p. 119.

44 A point also noted by Cobb (1988), p. 164.

45 Brownmiller, p. 149.

46 Women's menopause experiences of vaginal wetness/dryness appear to range over a continuum from problematic to no changes at all, with most women somewhere in the middle. As Cobb (1988) notes, the safest remedies for dry vagina, and urinary leakage, are a combination of regular orgasm (which encourages natural lubrication) and Kegel exercises (described in a number of women's health publications, including Cobb, Gerson, and Sachs).

47 Sontag, as quoted in Posner (1984), p. 70.

48 Menter, M. in *Redbook* (October, 1991), p. 3.

49 Menter, M. in *Redbook* (October, 1991), p. 62.

50 Menter, M. in *Redbook* (October, 1991), p. 65-66.

51 Miller, J.B. p. 83.

52 Miller, J.B. p. 87.

53 Gilligan (1982), p. 8.

54 Stevens-Long, p. 14.

55 Stevenson, p. 183.

56 Belenky et Al, pp. 6-7.

57 Such as, among others, Jean Baker Miller; Belenky, Clinchy, Goldberger & Tarule; Carol Gilligan; the researchers at the Stone Center, Wellesley College, Wellesley, Massachusetts.

58 Miller, J.B., p. 4.

59 Miller, J.B., p. 2.

60 Gilligan (1982), p. 6.

61 Stevens-Long, p. 20.

62 Stevens-Long, p. 20.

63 Stevens-Long, p. 6.

64 Hancock, p. 14.

65 Ussher, p. 107.

66 Quoted in Weideger, p. 213.

67 Aisenberg and Harrington; Brownmiller; Belenky et Al; Gilligan (1990).

68 Sachs in Brownmiller, p. 116.

69 Brownmiller, p. 118.

70 Aisenberg and Harrington, p. 65.

71 In Gilligan (1990).

72 Gilligan (1990), pp. 10-25.

73 Desrochers, p. 50.

74 Desrochers, p. 63.

75 A point also made by Hancock, pp. 33-34.

76 Gilligan (1990), p. 4.

77 Hancock, p. 4.

78 Lorde, p. 41.

79 Simmons, C. (1983). *New York Times Magazine.* In Freedman, p. 204.

80 Cobb, in *A Friend Indeed,* Sep. 91, p. 2.

81 Turner, p. 4.

82 van Gennep, in Turner.

83 Maslow, p. 95.

84 Maslow, p. 96.

85 Stevens-Long, p. 441.

86 Cobb, J. (June, 1992). *A Friend Indeed Newsletter.*

87 Martin, p. 130.

88 In Worden.

89 In Ussher.

90 Burnside, p. 40.

91 As reported in Airola, p. 409.

92 Ussher, p. 139.

93 *The Physician's Manual for Patients: The Standard Physician's Source Book of Symptoms, Diagnosis and Treatment.* (1984). New York: Times Books., p. 392.

94 Sanford, p. 4.

95 Pert, p. 16.

96 Martin, p. 170.

97 Wilber, K. & T. Wilber, p. 54.

98 Wilber, K. & T. Wilber, p. 88.

99 Martin; Posner.

100 Martin; Salk, Sanford, Swenson & Luce (1984), among others.

101 Martin, pp. 40-41.

102 Martin, p. 47.

103 Martin, pp. 49-50.

104 Martin, p. 50.

105 Martin, p. 51.

106 Eskin (1988), p. xiii.

107 Eskin (1988), p. viii-xii.

108 Berkow, p. 1714.

109 *Journal of the American Medical Association* (1990), p. 708.

110 Ettinger, B. and Grady, D, *New England Journal of Medicine* (1993), pp. 1192-1193.

111 Cobb, J.O. "Women at Midlife: Consumers of Second-Rate Health Care?" *A Friend Indeed*, Sept. 91., p. 3.
112 Prior, (in press).
113 Schlossberg, pp. 74-75.
114 Martin, p. 102.
115 Quotation in Martin (1987), p. 102.
116 *Webster's II New Riverside Dictionary* (1984).
117 By Neugarten and Kraines, in Weideger, pp. 200-201.
118 In McCrea.
119 In Berkun.
120 In Kaufert & McKinlay.
121 In Grossman & Bart.
122 In Berkun.
123 In Kaufert & McKinlay.
124 Kaufert & McKinlay, p. 121.
125 Kaufert & McKinlay, p. 134.
126 Ussher, p. 111.
127 Cobb (1986), p. 19.
128 Cobb (1986), p. 19.
129 Arms (1975), pp. 145-46.
130 Freedman, p. 222.
131 Schaef, p. 96.
132 Barthel, p. 60.
133 Freedman, p. 221.
134 Melamed, p. 158.
135 Melamed, p. 157.
136 Burnside, p. 104.
137 Freedman, p. 206.
138 Aldrich, p. 57.
139 Aldrich, p. 60.
140 Unfortunately, I am unable to locate the source of this quote. My apologies to Maxine Cumin.
141 Reitz, p. 72.
142 Atwood, p. 158.
143 Martin, p. 35.
144 Taylor, p. 109.
145 Martin, p. 197.
146 Melamed, p. 158.
147 Martin, p. 137.
148 LeGuin, U. (Summer, 1976). The Space crone. *Co-Evolution Quarterly*.

Bibliography

A Friend Indeed: A Newsletter for Women in the Prime of Life. P.O. Box 1710 Champlain, New York, 12929-1710; or P. O. Box 515, Place du Parc Station, Montreal, Quebec H2W 2P1.

Airola, P. (1979). *Everywoman's book.* Phoenix, Arizona: Health Plus Publishers.

Aisenberg, N., & Harrington, M. (1988). *Women of academe: Outsiders in the sacred grove.* Amherst: The University of Massachusetts Press.

Aldrich, N. W., Jr. (1992, January). The Je Ne Sais Quoi of European Beauty. *Lear's,* pp. 54-62.

Allan, J. & Dyck P. (1987). Transition from childhood to adolescence: Developmental curriculum. In L. C. Mahdi, S. Foster & M. Little (Eds.), *Betwixt & between: Patterns of masculine and feminine initiation* (pp. 23-43). La Salle, ILL: Open Court.

Allender, J. S. (1987). The evolution of research methods for the study of human experience. *Journal of Humanistic Psychology, 27* (4), 458-484.

Arms, S. (1975). *Immaculate Deception: A New Look at Women and Childbirth in America.* Boston: Houghton Mifflin.

Atwood, M. (1989, November). Weight. *Chatelaine,* p. 158.

Auel, J. M.)1980). *Clan of the cave bear.* New York: Crown.

Barthel, D. (1988). *Putting on appearances: Gender and advertising.* Philadelphia: Temple University Press.

Beane, W. C. & Doty, W. G. (Eds.). (1975). *Myths, rites, symbols: A Mircea Eliade reader.* New York: Harper Colophone Books.

Becker, C.S. (1987). *The invisible drama: Women and the anxiety of change.* New York: Macmillan.

Belenky, M. F., Clinchy, B. M., Goldberger, N. R. & Tarule, J. M. (1986) *Women's ways of knowing: The development of self, voice, and mind.* New York: Basic Books.

Bell, S. E. (1987). Changing ideas: The medicalization of menopause. *Social Science and Medicine, 24* (6), 535-542.

Berkow, R. (Ed.). (1987). *The Merck manual of diagnosis and therapy.* (15th ed.). Rahway, NJ: Merck.

Berkun, C. S. (1986). In behalf of women over 40: Understanding the importance of the menopause. *Social Work, 31* (5), 378-384.

Berman, M. (1984). *The reenchantment of the world.* Toronto: Bantam.

Bernard, J. (1975). *Women, wives and mothers: Values and options.* Hawthorne, N.Y.: Aldine de Gruyter.

Beyene, Y. (1986). Cultural significance and physiological manifestations of menopause: A biocultural analysis. *Culture, Medicine & Psychiatry, 10* (1), 47-71.

Beyene, Y. (1989). *From menarche to menopause: Reproductive lives of peasant women in two cultures.* New York: State University of New York Press.

Boston Women's Health Book Collective (1984). *The new our bodies, ourselves: A book by and for women.* New York: Simon & Schuster.

Bridges, W. (1980). *Transitions: Making sense of life's changes.* Don Mills, Ont.: Addison-Wesley.

Brown, J. K. (1982). A cross-cultural exploration of the end of the child-bearing years. In A. M. Voda, M. Dinnerstein & S. R. O'Donnell (Eds.), *Changing perspectives on menopause* (pp. 51-59). Austin: University of Texas Press.

Brownmiller, S. (1984). *Femininity.* New York: Simon & Schuster.

Burnside, B. (1990). *Depression is a femininst issue.* Vancouver, B.C.: Mature Women's Network.

Chodorow, N. (1978). *The reproduction of mothering.* Berkeley: University of California Press.

Cobb, J.O. (1993). *Understanding Menopause: Answers and advice for women in the prime of life.* New York: Penguin.

Cobb, J. O. (1986). The great hormone debate. *Healthsharing: A Canadian Women's Health Quarterly, 8* (1), 17-20.

Cobb, J. O. (1988). *Understanding menopause.* Toronto: Key Porter Books.

Cochran, L. & Claspell, E. (1987). *The meaning of grief: A dramaturgical approach to understanding emotion.* New York: Greenwood Press.

Colaizzi, P. F. (1978). Psychological research as the phenomenologist views it. In R. S. Valle & M. King (Eds.), *Existential-phenomenological alternatives for psychology* (pp. 48-71). New York: Oxford University Press.

Corey, G. (1985). *Theory and practice of group counselling* (2nd ed.). Monteray, CA: Brooks-Cole.

Daly, M. (1978). *Gyn/Ecology: The metaethics of radical feminism.* Boston: Beacon Press.

Davis, D. L. (1986). The meaning of menopause in a Newfoundland fishing village. *Culture, Medicine & Psychiatry, 10* (1), 73-94.

DeLorey, C. (1984). Health care and midlife women. In G. Baruch & J. Brooks-Gunn (Eds.), *Women in midlife* (pp. 277-301). New York: Plenum.

DeMarco, C. (1991). *Take charge of your body, a guide to women's health (Rev. ed.).* Winlaw, B.C.: The Last Laugh, Inc.

Desrochers, R. (1991). Voice: A single case narrative study. Unpublished thesis. Department of Counselling Psychology, University of British Columbia.

Deutsch, H. (1945). *The psychology of women: Vol. II Motherhood.* New York: Grune & Stratton.

Doress, P. B., Siegal, D. L. & The Midlife and Older Women Book Project (Eds.), (1987). *Ourselves, growing older: Women aging with knowledge and power.* New York: Simon & Schuster.

Downing, C. (1987). *Journey through menopause: A personal rite of passage.* New York: Crossroad.

Duff, J. (1987). Menopause & the media. *A Friend Indeed,* 4 (5), 1-6.

Eagan, A. B. (1989, April). The estrogen fix. *Ms,* pp. 38-43.

Eliade, M. (1975). *Rites and symbols of initiation.* New York: Harper Torchbooks.

Eskin, B. A. (Ed.). (1988). *The menopause: Comprehensive management.* New York: Macmillan.

Ettinger, B. & Grady, D. (1993). The waning effect of postmenopausal estrogen therapy on osteoporosis. *New England Journal of Medicine,* 329 (16), 1192-1194.

Fink, P. J. (1988). Psychiatric myths of the menopause. In B. A. Eskin (Ed.), *The menopause: Comprehensive management* (pp. 81-99). New York: Macmillan.

Flint, M. (1982). Male and female menopause: a cultural put-on. In A. M. Voda, M. Dinnerstein & S. R. O'Donnell (Eds.), *Changing perspectives on menopause* (pp. 363-375). Austin: University of Texas Press.

Freedman, R. (1986). *Beauty bound.* Toronto: D.C. Heath.

Gerson, M. (1990). *Menopause: A well woman book.* Toronto: Montreal Health Press.

Gilligan, C. (1982). *In a different voice: Psychological theory and women's development.* Cambridge, MA: Harvard University Press.

Gilligan, C. (1990). Teaching Shakespeare's sister: Notes from the underground of female adolescence. In C. Gilligan, N. Lyons & T. Hanmer (Eds.), *Making connections: The relational worlds of adolescent girls at Emma Willard School.* MA: Harvard University Press.

Gornick, V. (1973). *In Search of Ali Mahmoud.* NY: Saturday Review Press.

Greenwood, S. (1989). *Menopause naturally: Preparing for the second half of life* (rev. ed.). Volcano, CA: Volcano Press.

Grossman, M. & Bart, P. G. (1982). Taking the men out of menopause. In R. Hubbard, M. S. Henifin & B. Fried (Eds.), *Biological women: The convenient myth* (pp. 187-198). Cambridge, MA: Schenkman.

Hall, S. S. (1989). A molecular code links emotions, mind and health. *Smithsonian, 20* (3), 62-71.

Hamilton, J. A., Parry, B. L. & Blumenthal, S. J. (1988). The menstrual cycle in context, I: Affective syndromes associated with reproductive hormonal changes. *Journal of Clinical Psychiatry, 49* (12), 474-480.

Hancock, E. (1989). *The girl within: Recapture the childhood self, the key to female identify.* New York: Dutton.

Healthsharing: A Canadian Women's Health Quarterly (Spring '91). 14 Skey Lane, Toronto, Ontario, M6J 3S4.

Hitchman, J (1975). *Such a Strange Lady: A biography of Dorothy L. Sayers.* Great Britain: Hodder & Stoughton.

Huyck, M. H. & Hoyer, W. J. (1982). *Adult development and aging.* Belmont, CA: Wadsworth.

Jaggar, A. M. (1983). *Feminist politics and human nature.* Sussex, England: The Harvester Press.

Jung, C. (1933). *Modern man in search of a soul.* New York: Harcourt Brace.

Kaufert, P. A. (1982). Myth and the menopause. *Sociology of Health and Illness. 4* (2).

Kaufert, P. A. & Gilbert, P. (1986). Women, menopause, and medicalization. *Culture, Medicine and Psychiatry, 10* (1), 7-21.

Kaufert, P. A. & McKinlay, S. M. (1985). Estrogen-replacement therapy: the production of medical knowledge and the emergence of policy. In E. Lewin & V. Olesen (Eds.), *Women, health and healing: Toward a new perspective* (pp. 113-138). New York: Travistock.

Kincaid-Ehlers, E. (1982). Bad maps for an unknown region: Menopause from a literary perspective. In A. M. Voda, M. Dinnerstein & S. R. O'Donnell (Eds.), *Changing perspectives on menopause* (pp. 24-37). Austin: University of Texas Press.

Lakoff, G. & Johnson, M. (1980). *Metaphors we live by.* Chicago: University of Chicago Press.

Lakoff, R. T. & R. L. Scherr (1984). *Face value: The politics of beauty.* Boston: Routledge & Kegan Paul.

Langone, J. & Horowitz, J. M. (1989, August 14). Hard looks at hormones. *Time,* p. 48.

Lennon, M. C. (1982). The psychological consequences of menopause: The importance of timing of a life stage event. *Journal of Health and Social Behavior, 23,* 353-366.

Lennon, M. C. (1987). Is menopause depressing? An investigation of three perspectives. *Sex Roles, 17* (1/2), 1-16.

Lessing, D. (1975). *The Summer Before Dark.* Harmondsworth: Penguin.

Levinson, D. J. (1986). A conception of adult development. *American Psychologist, 41* (1), 3-13.

Lock, M. (1991, Spring). Letter to the editor. *Healthsharing: A Canadian Women's Health Quarterly.*

Lock, M. (1982). Models and practice in medicine: Menopause as a syndrome or life transition? *Culture, Medicine & Psychiatry, 6,* 261-280.

Lock, M. (1986a). Ambiquities of aging: Japanese experience and perceptions of menopause. *Culture, Medicine & Psychiatry, 10* (1), 23-46.

Lock, M. (1986b). Introduction. *Culture, Medicine & Psychiatry, 10* (1), 1-5.

Lorde, A. (1984). *Sister Outsider: Essays and Speeches.* Turmansburg, N.Y.: Crossing Press.

Mallory, L. (1984). *Leading self-help groups: A guide for training facilitators.* New York: Family Service America.

Managing Menopause (pamphlet: no date available). Ayerst Laboratories, Division of Ayerst, McKenna & Harrison, Inc., Montreal, Canada.

Martin, E. (1987). *The woman in the body: A cultural analysis of reproduction.* Boston: Beacon Press.

Maslow, A. (1962). Emotional blocks to creativity. In S. J. Parnes & H. F. Harding (Eds.). *A source book for creative thinking.* New York: Charles Scribners.

McCrea, F. B. (1983). The politics of menopause: The "discovery" of a deficiency disease. *Social Problems, 31* (1), 111-123.

McKinlay, J. B. & McKinlay, S. M. (1987). Depression in middle-aged women: Social circumstances versus estrogen deficiency. In M. R. Walsh (Ed.), *The psychology of women: ongoing debates* (pp. 157-161). New Haven, CT: Yale.

McKinlay, J. B. & McKinlay, S. M. (1989). Depression in middle-aged women. *A Friend Indeed, 6* (7), 1-3.

McKinlay, S. M. & McKinlay, J. B. (1973). Selected studies of the menopause. *Journal of Biosocial Science, 5*, 533-555.

Melamed, E. (1983). *Mirror, mirror: The terror of not being young.* New York: Simon & Schuster.

Miller, A. (1986). *Thou shalt not be aware: Society's betrayal of the child.* (trans. by Hildegarde & Hunter Hannum). New York: Farrar, Straus & Giroux.

Miller, J. B. (1986). *Toward a new psychology of women* (2nd ed.). Boston: Beacon Press.

Mishler, E. G. (1986). *Research interviewing: Context and narrative.* Cambridge, MA: Harvard University Press.

Moss, D. (1978). Brain, body, and world: Perspectives on body-image. In R. S. Valle & M. King (Eds.), *Existential-phenomenological alternatives for psychology* (pp. 73-93). New York: Oxford University Press.

Nagy, M. (1987). Menstruation and shamanism. In L. C. Mahdi, S. Foster & M. Little (Eds.), *Betwixt & between: Patterns of masculine and feminine initiation* (pp. 223-238). La Salle, ILL: Open Court.

Neugarten, B. L., Wood, V., Draines, R. J. & Loomis, B. (1968). Women's attitudes toward the menopause. In B. L. Neugarten (Ed.), *Middle age and aging* (pp. 195-200). Chicago: University of Chicago Press.

Pert, C. (no date available). *Neuropeptides: The emotions and bodymind.* In Psychoneuroimmunology: The Scientific Basis of Holism in Medicine. Published by the American Holistic Medical Association.

Porcino, J. (1983). *Growing older, getting better: A handbook for women in the second half of life.* Don Mills, Ont.: Addison-Wesley.

Posner, J. (1979). It's all in your head: Feminist and medical models of menopause (strange bedfellows). *Sex Roles, 5* (2), 179-190.

Prior, J.C. (in press). One voice on menopause. *Journal of the American Medical Women's Association.*

Reitz, R. (1977). *Menopause: A positive approach.* Markham, Ont.: Penguin.

Reuter, J. & Zak, M. W. (1982). Erik Erikson and Doris Lessing: Psychological theory and the female novel of development. In A. M. Voda, M. Dinnerstein & S. R. O'Donnell (Eds.), *Changing perspectives on menopause* (pp. 170-186). Austin: University of Texas Press.

Rich, A. (1986). *Of woman born: Motherhood as experience and institution (10th ed).* New York: Norton.

Rogers, C. R. (1985). Toward a more human science of the person. *Journal of Humanistic Psychology, 25* (4), 7-24.

Rubin, L. B. (1979). *Women of a certain age: The midlife search for self.* New York: Harper & Row.

Sachs, J. (1991). *What women should know about menopause.* New York: Bantam.

Salk, H., Sanford, W., Swenson, N., & Luce, J. D. (1984). The politics of women and medical care. In Boston Women's Health Book Collective, *The new our bodies, ourselves* (pp. 555-597). New York: Simon & Schuster.

Sanford, W. (1984). Introduction. In Boston Women's Health Book Collective, *The new our bodies, ourselves* (p.3-4). New York: Simon & Schuster.

Schaef, A.W. (1985). *Women's reality: An emerging female system in a white male society.* New York: Harper & Row.

Schlossberg, N. K. (1987, May). Taking the mystery out of change. *Psychology Today.*

Severne, L. (1982). Psychosocial aspects of the menopause. In A. M. Voda, M. Dinnerstein & S. R. O'Donnell (Eds.), *Changing perspectives on menopause* (pp. 239-247). Austin: University of Texas Press.

Sheehy, G. (1992). *The silent passage: Menopause.* New York: Random House.

Siegal, D. L., Costlow, J., Lopez, M. C., Taub, M. & Kronenberg, F. (1987). Menopause: Entering our third age. In P. B. Doress & D. L. Siegal (Eds.), *Ourselves, growing older: Women aging with knowledge and power* (pp. 116-126). Toronto: Simon & Schuster.

Sontag, S. (1979). The double standard of aging. In J. Williams (Ed.), *Psychology of women: Selected readings,* (pp. 462-479). New York: W.W. Norton.

Stevens-Long, J. (1984). *Adult life: Developmental processes* (2nd ed.). Los Angeles, CA: Mayfield.

Stevenson, J. S. (1977). *Issues and crises during middlescence.* New York: Appleton-Century-Crofts.

Stimpson, C. R. (1982). The fallacy of bodily reductionism. In A. M. Voda, M. Dinnerstein & S. R. O'Donnell (Eds.), *Changing perspectives on menopause* (pp. 265-272). Austin: University of Texas Press.

Sullivan, E. V. (1984). *A critical psychology: Interpretation of the personal world*. New York: Plenum.

Taylor, D. (1988). *Red flower: Rethingking menstruation*. Freedom, CA: Crossing Press.

Thomson, S. (1986). Sharing the menopause experience. *Health-sharing: A Canadian Women's Health Quarterly*, *8* (1), 10-13.

Turner, V. (1987). Betwixt and between: The liminal period in rites of passage. In L. C. Mahdi, S. Foster & M. Little (Eds.), *Betwixt & between: patterns of masculine and feminine initiation* (pp. 3-19). La Salle, ILL: Open Court.

Unger, R. (1985). Personal appearance and social control. In M. Safir, M. Mednick, D. Izraeli, & J. Bernard (Eds.), *Women's Worlds: The new Scholarship*. New York: Praeger.

Ussher, J. M. (1989). *The psychology of the female body*. New York: Routledge.

Walsh, M. R. (1987). Is the menopause a deficiency disease? In M. R. Walsh (Ed.), *The psychology of women: Ongoing debates* (pp. 147-149). New Haven, CT: Yale.

Weideger, P. (1976). *Menstruation and menopause: The physiology and psychology, the myth and reality*. New York: Knopf.

Wilber K. & T. (September/October, 1988). Do we make ourselves sick? *New Age Journal*.

Williams, T. F. (1990). Osteoporosis and hip fractures: Challenges to investigators and clinicians. *Journal of the American Medical Association*, *263* (5), 708.

Wilson, R. (1966). *Feminine forever*. New York: M. Evans.

Worden, J. W. (1982). *Grief counselling and grief therapy: A handbook for the mental health practitioner*. New York: Springer

Lafern Page has a Master of Arts degree in Counselling

Psychology from the University of British Columbia.

She lives in Vancouver, B.C. where she is in private

practice, working with both individuals and groups.

She also delivers talks and leads workshops on topics

related to women and menopause.

Index

Order Form

for

Menopause and Emotions: Making Sense of Your Feelings When Your Feelings Make No Sense

Please send _____ copies
  @$19.95 per copy   = $ _____.____

G.S.T.:   add 7%   = $ _____.____

Provincial tax:
  Quebec residents add 8%   = $ _____.____

Shipping:
  add $3.00 for 1 - 3 books   = $ _____.____

For orders of 4 or more
books, add an additional
$1.00 per book   = $ _____.____

                    TOTAL   = $ _____.____

MAIL your order to:

Primavera Press
P.O. Box 74672
2803 West 4th Avenue
Vancouver, B.C. V6K 4P4

SEND my book(s) to:

Name _____

Address _____

City _____ Prov./State _____

          Postal/Zip Code _____